THE STORY
GUY'S HOSPITAL
NURSES' LEAGUE
1900–2010

League Council at their final meeting – September 2010

THE STORY OF GUY'S HOSPITAL NURSES' LEAGUE
1900–2010

By
ANDIE HOWARD

First published in 2010 by
GHNL

British Library Cataloguing in Publication Data
A C.I.P. for this book is available from the British Library

ISBN 978-0-9567318-0-7

Typeset and produced by
The Studio Publishing Services Ltd
www.publishingservicesuk.co.uk

Printed in Great Britain

This book is dedicated to all members
of Guy's Hospital Nurses' League
Past and Present

With a special mention to Betty Herbert,
who died on September 27th 2010 having served
the League as Honorary Secretary, Chairman and
President from 1972–1995

Contents

Acknowledgements

Many thanks to all Officers and Council of the League for their information, photographs, help and encouragement; the British Journal of Nursing historical editions at the RCN Archives; the London Metropolitan Archives; Guy's Gazette bi-centenary edition; the Nursing Times 1907–1914 editions, Bill Edwards for photographs, Mavis Fabling for the books, Brenda Faulkner and Alison Russell for assisting with the archives, Betsy Morley for her contribution to Chapter 11 and Daphne Hutson for her donation.

Preface

Nurses' Leagues were founded in the early part of the twentieth century when formal three year training for nurses was introduced and they began to feel a strong allegiance to the hospitals where they received their training. The nurses wished to maintain links with these institutions and the friends and colleagues they had made there, who, on qualifying, would acquire nursing posts throughout the UK and indeed throughout the world.

The Guy's Hospital Nurses' League, formed in 1900, served three purposes. It brought existing nursing clubs and societies together, provided a register with details of all nurses who trained at Guy's and organised an Annual General Meeting when Guy's nurses could assemble to keep in touch with the hospital and their colleagues.

The League remained an integral part of the nursing world at Guy's throughout the 20th century and was valued and supported by many generations of Guy's nurses.

But times change and in the 1990s, nurse education became university based; the traditional nursing schools were closed and the last set of Guy's nurses qualified in 1996.

Within the new system nurses received their clinical experience in various hospitals so no longer identified with one particular institution and were therefore not interested in joining a particular Nurses' League. At Guy's, new membership was declining and the current members, who were aging fast, struggled to provide Officers and Council members to run the League. With decreased numbers, income from membership fees was also reduced.

After a number of years of discussion and soul searching and with all possible options considered it was decided that a date should be selected to close the Guy's League rather than let it decline slowly and 2010 was chosen to be the final year. Although this was a difficult and heartfelt decision the general mood was to celebrate the life of the League rather lament than its closure. It was determined that the final AGM in 2010 should involve a huge celebration to commemorate the League and its members.

Introduction

Towards the end of the 19th century there was an atmosphere of change and development in nursing. For years 'nurses' had been ill-educated drudges known for their dishonesty and drunkenness. There was need for drastic reform and it was just around the corner.

Gradually things were improving. At Guy's, in the 1870's, Dr Steele, the Superintendent started a series of lectures for the nurses and a sequence of dynamic and reforming Matrons battled to improve the conditions and training.

By 1898 Guy's nurses were receiving lectures on nursing, medicine, surgery, and dispensing. The nurses' schedule, a record of practical experience, was introduced and formal examinations took place with a certificate awarded to successful candidates.

At the same time, under the influence of Florence Nightingale, well educated women of social standing were entering nursing and it began to be thought of as a suitable profession for young ladies. Influential and progressive Sisters and Matrons were appointed from these nurses.

At Guy's it was realised that this new breed of nurses required nurturing and that the provision of activities for relaxation and entertainment for when they were not on duty were essential to maintain their physical and mental health. So in the late 1890s a number of clubs and societies were formed, including the Lawn Tennis & Croquet Club, the Cycling Club and the Choral Society.

Meanwhile Miss Isla Stewart, the Matron of St Bartholomew's Hospital, Guy's close neighbour in the City of London, recognised that the nurses who trained there were developing a strong bond to the hospital and their colleagues. She felt they would value an organisation that enabled them to maintain their links with the institution and to this end, she founded the St Bartholomew's Nurses' League in 1899. Her principles were to encourage high standards of work by nursing collaboration, to promote mutual help and pleasure and to provide benevolence for former Bart's nurses.

In 1900 Sarah Swift became Matron of Guy's and soon after she formed a similar organisation called the Guy's Hospital Past and Present Nurses' League.

CHAPTER ONE

The Preceding Years

The years prior to the formation of the League saw major change and development in nursing at Guy's, greatly influenced by a number of strong willed and forward thinking Matrons. These inspirational women paved the way for the founding of the League. They made nurses take pride in their work, feel an important member of the hospital team and develop a sense of belonging to the institution where they trained and worked.

Miss Margaret Elizabeth Burt, Matron 1879–1882

Margaret Burt was a remarkable and formidable woman. Soon after her appointment she made her intentions clear. She wanted to create a Matron's Office that managed all nursing affairs and she emphasised the need for proper training for nurses. She felt that the Matron should be a key player in the hospital administration together with the Hospital Treasurer and Superintendent. She had the support of Edward Hearbord Lushington, the Guy's Treasurer at the time and together they advocated what was called 'The New System of Nursing Administration'. There was huge opposition from the sisters, who felt their power would be diminished in this scheme and the medical staff who wanted to continue to exercise their control over nursing on the wards. This internal storm reached the National Press and raged on for several months.

Miss Burt stood her ground and despite the opposition, and her somewhat undiplomatic approach, the system was implemented, Matron's office was created and formal nurse training commenced. The latter eventually led to the formation of a Guy's Nurse Training School.

In 1882 Miss Burt resigned as Matron of Guy's to marry Mr Alfred Field.

Margaret Elizabeth Burt 1839–1890

Margaret Elizabeth Burt was born on July 2nd 1839 at Southall Green, Middlesex, where her father, the Rev John Thomas Burt was the curate. She was the eldest of fourteen children. Margaret spent much of her childhood with her grandparents in Devon but returned to her family home, aged 18 on the death of her grandmother. By this time her father was Chaplain of the Birmingham Borough Jail and the family lived in Winston Green, Birmingham.

A few years later she took on the running of a local home for troublesome girls. In 1871, having always wanted to be a properly trained nurse, she went for a month's probation at St Thomas' Hospital. After the month she decided she would prefer to be trained by the St John's Sisters who had charge of King's College and Charing Cross Hospitals, so she entered King's as a lady pupil.

She developed quickly, one of the doctors remarking that she had learnt more in three months than others would in six. Within a year she was promoted to ward sister. For the next three years she worked at King's and Charing Cross, including being in charge of the whole of the latter hospital for short periods.

In June 1874 she felt her primary duty was to earn money for her family and she accepted the post of Superintendent of a Home for Private Nurses in Leicester. She immediately made an impact and recognising that there was no prospect of improving the Institution without some formal training for the nurses, she proposed to the Committee and leading medical men in the town that her Institution should provide nurses for the local Infirmary. Within six weeks that whole hospital was under her care. She had the medical staff and Committee eating out of her hand and they remained her firm friends and supporters for the rest of her life.

Her reputation was such in the medical world that Mr Edward Lushington, the Treasurer of Guy's earnestly requested that she move to Guy's as Matron and although reluctant to leave Leicester, the opportunity was too good to miss and she agreed.

At Guy's she again made an immediate impact but did not receive the support that she had at Leicester. However she persisted and in the end had her way and the result was the beginning of formal nurse education at Guy's.

In 1882, in her forties, Margaret received a wedding proposal from Mr Alfred Field and she left Guy's to get married. They wed in 1883 but sadly he died two years later. Margaret although suffering from severe rheumatoid arthritis acted as Matron at Charing Cross Hospital for a time before she too died in 1890 at the early age of 51.

Forty one years after her death, the British Journal of Nursing of February 1931, published an article about her as one of the forgotten 'warriors' of nursing development, who had championed the modernisation of nursing in the late 19th century. The language of the article is dramatically descriptive: '*it is hoped that in time, due recognition will be accorded to these forceful explorers and pioneers, who fought with beasts at Ephesus, and suffered many wounds*' [1]

Margaret Elizabeth Burt

Miss Victoria Elizabeth Jones, Matron 1882–1893

Miss Jones had worked at Leicester with Miss Burt and followed her to Guy's where she was appointed into a Sister's post. She loyally supported Miss Burt during the turmoil of her re-organisation of nursing. She was blessed with a quiet devotion to duty and had gained the admiration and respect of the hospital authorities, so was immediately promoted as Matron when Miss Burt resigned to get married.

The position and conditions of nurses continued to improve during Miss Jones time in office. When she left the post a popular nursing magazine, *The Nursing Record*, in its February 2nd 1893 publication, wrote that her resignation would be sincerely regretted by her colleagues:

> *'it is universally acknowledged that she has performed the arduous duties connected with her post, in the most conscientious and devoted manner'.* [2]

It goes on to add that the Matron's post at Guy's is the most laborious and worst paid in London!

Miss Victoria Jones

In 1893 Victoria Jones resigned as Matron to go and look after her two sisters who were in ill health and she was succeeded by Florence Nott-Bower.

There was an interesting incident involving the nursing staff during Miss Jones time as Matron although she was not directly involved. It demonstrated that in the latter part of the 19th century nurses were beginning to assert themselves more and that the new breed of nurses were prepared to act together and challenge the authorities – albeit in the mildest, politest manner.

It began with a letter from one of the nurses of the Guy's Hospital Trained Nurses' Institution, which was established in 1884 by Edward Lushington, the Hospital Treasurer. His introductory memorandum for the Institution had stated:

> 'The Governors of Guy's Hospital have sanctioned the establishment of a Nursing Institution in connection with the hospital, wholly independent of the Hospital for its support, though subject to Regulations to be approved by the Governors.
>
> The objects of the Institution were: to provide the public with skilled nurses trained in the hospital and of good character, to supply the hospital with extra nurses when required in emergencies and remove the need to hire casual nursing staff, and to provide nursing free of charge to those in the locality who could not afford other care'.[3]

It seems to have been some sort of early 'nursing agency'.

The nurses received board and lodging and training from the Hospital. The Lady Superintendent of the Institution was Florence Nott-Bower, later to be Matron of Guy's, although the Institution remained under the direct control of Mr Lushington.

The events began in 1892 when a nurse called Ellen Mayne, and several other of her colleagues, who are unnamed, sent a petition regarding their pay to Mr Lushington and copied it to the Lady Superintendent. The gist of the letter was that they had been underpaid and had been expecting an increase in salary for some time. They had spoken to the Lady Superintendent about this on several occasions over the past two years without effect. Nurse Mayne had been one of the first nurses to join the Institution in 1884 and claimed that, by 1892 she should have received about £620 but had received less than £220.

The nurses asked that as the Institution had a healthy balance, those with over four years of service should receive an annual increase of £40.

The response from the Treasurer was terse and dismissive. He did not respond to the nurses but forwarded the petition to Miss Nott-Bower asking her to inform them that they had acted wrongly in writing directly to him and that any applications should be sent through her.

The Lady Superintendent supported this view and replied to Nurse Mayne that any further communication must be directed to herself or Matron. She reiterated that the issue of nurses' pay had been under the consideration of the Treasurer and no change was likely before the end of the financial year.

Poor Ellen Mayne seems to have taken the rap for this infringement and handed in her notice. However she had not finished with the matter and wrote to the Nursing Record, explaining the situation and enclosing copies of all the correspondence.

Her letters were published in the Nursing Record of 3rd November 1892 under the title *'Charitable Sweating'*.[4] The indomitable Mrs Bedford Fenwick, who was the Editor of this publication, soon to be re-named The British Journal of Nursing (BJN), was outraged and her editorial was vociferous in her criticism of Mr Lushington.

She first gave support to the Matron, Miss Victoria Jones and Florence Nott-Bower, the Lady Superintendent, writing that they were highly thought of and exonerating them of all blame in the matter.

She went on to describe the government of the Nursing Institution as *'antediluvian'* and *'a densely ignorant autocracy'*[4] She even quoted a Select Committee of the House of Lords who had expressed concern about the administration at Guy's giving too much power and responsibility to one individual, namely, the Treasurer.

She became more impassioned on her subject, referring back to Thomas Guy, writing that:

> *'Old Thomas Guy would doubtless groan in the spirit if he were aware that the splendid Institution, founded upon his benevolence, had, at the end of the 19th century, been converted into a commercial concern, grinding the face of its women workers – greedily grasping all it could sweat out of its white slaves, and when they were broken down, tossing them aside like worn-out goods'.*[4]

A little strong perhaps but Mrs Fenwick was a leader in nursing emancipation and she had already clashed publicly with Mr Lushington over nursing registration – so they had what would be described today as 'history'.

Two weeks later in the same magazine, Mr Lushington attempted to justify and rationalise his actions but Mrs Fenwick was unrelenting in rejecting the arguments in his letter and at the end of another lengthy and censorious editorial she concluded:

> 'It is clearly hopeless to discuss the matter further with this gentleman. It is notorious in professional circles how, like the lay managers of some other Institutions, he has opposed nursing reforms; how he has abrogated himself the right to speak with authority on nursing matters'.[5]

Edward Lushington's reputation should be defended. He had been a great supporter of Matron Burt in her efforts to reform and he had founded the Trained Nurses Institute. He was trying to keep Guy's going in the 1890s during a major depression when money was short, so one can see that an increase in nurses' pay, however justified, was not a priority for him at the time.

Mrs Bedford Fenwick

Edward Lushington

Victoria Elizabeth Jones 1838–1935

Victoria Jones was born in Carmarthen, Wales in 1837. She died in 1935 aged 98. She was described as an exceedingly able woman who would take hold of an onerous task with enthusiasm and success. Aged 30, she went into the Tractarian movement who helped the residents of the London slums. However she soon realised that her interest lay in nursing and she trained as a probationer at Charing Cross Hospital. Having worked as a staff nurse at Barts and Leicester she gained a Sister's post on Job ward at Guy's in 1880 and was promoted as Matron in 1882. In retirement she lived in Balham, South London and maintained her connection with Guy's and the Nurses' League for the rest of her life.

British Journal of Nursing Obituary – October 1935 [6]

Miss Florence C Nott-Bower, Matron 1893–1899

Miss Florence Nott-Bower

Florence Nott-Bower had been Lady Superintendent of the Guy's Trained Nurses Institute and replaced Miss Jones as Matron in 1893. Her six years as Matron saw many developments and improvements in nursing and in the lives and conditions of the nurses.

In 1893 every nurse was given a guaranteed fixed half day off once a week which they knew in advance. Previously if there was an emergency or staff shortages, the Ward Sister could withdraw this and frequently did.

Over the next few years many other improvements were introduced including regular holidays, a holiday allowance, a washable uniform and laundering services, better food, an increase in the nursing establishment and improved pay.

Following the appointment of Sir Cooper Perry as Superintendent in 1892, medical. surgical, dispensing and nursing lectures commenced and a stiff examination had to be passed. A nursing schedule, a record of practical experience was introduced which continued in a similar format well into the 1960s. Later lectures on specialist subjects and theatre nursing were also commenced.

Matron's Office and administration was given a boost by the introduction of an Assistant Matron and what would be called today Matron's P.A. in the form of Miss May Smith who was to be a long standing friend and support to the future Nurses' League, acting as clerk to the Treasurer and Honorary Secretary.

Until the late 1890s there were two systems of training for nurses at Guy's. The Lady Pupils who paid 13 guineas a quarter for a year's training and were awarded a certificate after one year that enabled them to work as trained nurses. The other group of nurses, the probationers, received three years training, and a small salary and also had to pass an examination on medical and surgical nursing. This system became the cause of much discontent among the nurses as the Lady Pupils tended to be promoted to senior nursing posts over the heads of other, more experienced nurses. The Lady Pupil played her part in improving nursing standards by introducing well educated, middle class women to nursing as a profession, but by the late 1890s she had had her day and this training was phased out.

In April 1899 the award of medals and prizes was made a public event and Miss Nott-Bower addressed the gathered nursing staff. This was noteworthy as it is thought to be the first time in the history of Guy's that a Matron had publicly addressed her nurses.

Miss Nott Bower was renowned for her forward thinking ideas, one of which was a babies' home for the children of the women who worked in the Laundry Hostel and elsewhere in the Hospital. A property known as "Shelford", 182 Devonshire Road, Honor Oak was purchased and the Home, known as "the Haven", was opened in November 1899.

By 1897 the nursing establishment had reached 197 and this resulted in an acute shortage of accommodation. The generous gift in 1897 of £20,000 from Mr Henry Raphael for nursing accommodation in memory of his wife, Henriette Raphael, was therefore most welcome. The original plans for this building were submitted to Miss Nott-Bower for her practical suggestions, prior to her retirement on health grounds in 1899.

On her retirement she was presented with a beautiful inscribed scroll by her colleagues.

Florence W C Nott-Bower 1857–1942

Florence was born in 1857 in Yorkshire, one of 7 children. Her father John Bower was a barrister and her mother Charlotte was born in Bengal, India although she was a British subject. By 1881 when Florence was 24, her father had died and the family moved to Lambeth, in London.

From 1883–1885 she was a Lady pupil at Guy's and after her training she became a Ward Sister there until 1888. In 1889 she was Matron of the Huddersfield Infirmary for a few months but she soon returned to Guy's as the first Lady Superintendent of the Trained Nurses' Institute.

She served as Matron from 1893–1899 when she retired from nursing aged 42, due to ill health. After leaving Guy's she worked in Africa for the South African Church Railway Mission, where she covered an area of 5,000 miles caring for the railway employees and their families.

After her missionary work, Florence spent the remainder of her days in Richmond, Surrey and died, aged 84 in 1941.

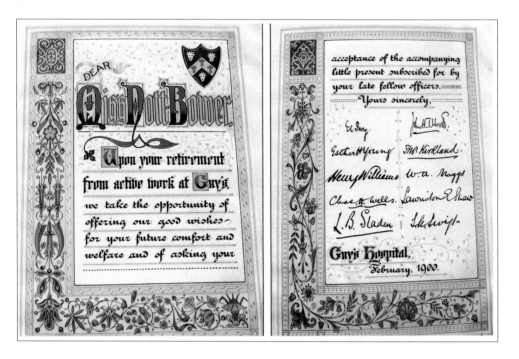

Florence Nott-Bower's scrolls

Miss Esther Young, Matron 1899–1900

As Miss Nott-Bower left her post at short notice in 1899, the Assistant Matron, Miss Esther Young became acting Matron while a replacement was being sought. Esther Young had been a valued Assistant Matron under Florence Nott-Bower.

She undertook research on behalf of the Governors, by visiting nursing schools in a number of major hospitals to gather ideas that might assist Matron Nott-Bower in her reforms at Guy's.

It is not known whether Miss Young aspired to the substantive post of Matron but on the appointment of Sarah Swift in 1900 she left the hospital. The Nursing Record of January 12th 1901 reports that:

> *'Miss Young will be a very real loss to the nursing staff of Guy's, by whom she is held in the greatest esteem and whose welfare she has had peculiarly at heart. Immense improvements have been made for the nurses' professional advancement and comfort, which have resulted from her powers of organization and administration'.*[7]

When she resigned the Sister's and nurses sent a statement to the Treasurer expressing their deep sense of loss.

Miss Esther Young

Esther Harriet Young. Born 1862

Esther Young was the youngest daughter of George Adam Young, an architect from London. Her brother was Keith Downes Young, also a well known hospital architect.

She was educated at private schools in Richmond and Worcester Park. Following school and before taking up a career in nursing, she spent time on visiting the poor and other parochial duties under the Vicar of Richmond.

She trained at Addenbrookes Hospital, Cambridge, where her sister, Mary Anna Young, was the Ward Sister of the main medical ward. Mary was an invaluable mentor to her younger sister.

Esther next went to the London Hospital but unfortunately contracted diphtheria from a patient, who was also a nurse. Following this illness she had to undertake lighter duties and she worked at the Throat Hospital and gained experience in private nursing at Gordon House under the redoubtable Mrs Bedford Fenwick.

In 1891 she returned to Addenbrookes as Assistant Matron with her old friend, Matron Cureton. Whilst there, on her birthday she was presented with a silver cream jug and sugar basin by the probationers as a token of their esteem for her. She went to Guy's as Assistant Matron in 1896.

CHAPTER TWO

Past and Present Nurses' League

During her time as Matron, Florence Nott-Bower had advocated recreation for the nursing staff and by 1898 a number of nurses' clubs and societies had been formed at Guy's. The committee of one of these, The Cycling Club, suggested that they all combine to form a club union. This then became the Recreation Society which held its first meeting on February 8th 1900. At this time, Esther Young was Matron, and the Honorary Secretary of the Recreation Society, and Sarah Swift, who was Lady Superintendent of the Trained Nurses' Institution, was on the Committee.

The wives of the Governors and other Hospital members were written to and asked for their support for the new Society and a bank account was opened at the London & County Bank.

In November 1901 at a Recreation Society Council Meeting Sarah Swift, who had been appointed as Matron, proposed that a union or association for past and present Guy's nurses be formed for the purpose of keeping them in touch with the Hospital. This would also include a register of all nurses who trained at Guy's.

A Sub-Committee was appointed to consider this proposal. The committee comprised, in the chair, Dr Lauriston Shaw, Dean of the Medical & Dental School, Matron, Sarah Swift, Sister Astley Cooper Ward and Nurse Layton.

On December 21st 1901 the Committee presented its report:

'Your Committee recommend that an Association of former members of the Nursing Staff be established in connection with the Recreation Society, and that the joint bodies be known as the 'Guy's Hospital Past and Present Nurses' League or Society'.

> *No alteration need be made in the Constitution of the Recreation Society, except that a Representative of the Past Nursing Staff should be annually co-opted by the Council.*
>
> *There would be two classes of Members of the League:– Probationers who would be Associates of the League; and Life Members of the League.*[8]

It goes on . . .

> '*The Committee recommend that if these proposals commend themselves to Council immediate steps be taken by advertisement and otherwise to obtain the names and addresses of former nurses, and to invite them to join the League, so that the first Register may be issued shortly after the Annual Meeting in March 1902'.*[8]

The proposal received a positive response from the Recreation Society Council and a meeting of all the current nurses was convened to explain its objectives and invite suggestions.

In February 1902 the proposal was put to the Recreation Club Council Committee by Mrs Shaw, wife of the Dean. It was seconded by Sarah Swift and accepted. A recommendation was then made to approach the House Committee suggesting that the Recreation Society should, in future, be known as the Guy's Hospital Past & Present Nurses' League.

Dame Sarah Swift

Sarah Swift wrote in her Matron's report:

'I am very anxious to start a register of the past and present Guy's nurses in association with the Recreation Society. I propose that the register shall contain a good deal of information useful to nurses as well as being a continuing link with each other and with the Hospital after they have left it.

I should be glad to have the permission of the House Committee to proceed with this scheme and I hope soon to be able to present a detailed account of what I wish to carry out'. [9]

There is no record of the comments of the House Committee but they must have been favourable as a report in the British Journal of Nursing, of July 19th 1902 announced the formation of the Guy's Hospital Past and Present Nurses' League.

The rules and regulations of the Recreation Society were amended and a League Constitution was written that laid down the rules and regulations for the members, the format of a Council to manage League affairs and the conditions and classes of membership.

A handbook was compiled that contained a register of all nurses who trained at Guy's. The concept of a register had long been an aspiration of Sarah Swift and even Mrs Fenwick acknowledged it as being a step in the right direction towards a register for all nurses, writing in her magazine that she had *'a pleasant thrill of surprise'* [10] when reading of it.

The first register included the names of around 700 nurses who had trained at Guy's plus another 163 associates who were in training or still worked at the Hospital. For each member there were brief biographical details with home addresses, dates of training, positions held etc. The register was then and remains now, a tool to help Guy's nurses keep in touch with their colleagues and friends.

The register was published in a book entitled: 'A Nursing Guide' which also included much information about nursing and patient care. This was the fore-runner of the Guy's Hospital Nurses' League Journal which was introduced in 1966.

The Guy's League of 1902 had major input from the Hospital administration, the Council comprising the Hospital Treasurer, the Superintendent, who was a doctor, and the Matron, who acted as Honorary Secretary, (all ex-officio) plus three members appointed by the House Committee.

GUY'S HOSPITAL
Past and Present Nurses' League 1903

President:
MRS. H. COSMO BONSOR

Patrons and Patronesses

THE COUNTESS OF BECTIVE	MRS EDWARDS
LORD BIDDULPH	MRS GALABIN
LORD COBHAM	MRS GOLDING-BIRD
HON. EDITH GIBBS	MRS GOODHART
THE HON. MRS TALBOT	ROBERT GORDON, Esq
LADY FREEMANTLE	E. HAMBRO, Esq
THE HON. LADY GULL	RODOLPH A. HANKEY, Esq
THE HON. EVELYN HUBBARD	MRS HANKEY
THE HON. ARTHUR J. BALFOUR	MRS HARVEY
LADY HOARE	MRS HIGGINS
SIR C. FREEMANTLE	P. HORROCKS, Esq, M.D.
SIR ALFRED FRIPP	MRS JACOBSON
LADY FRIPP	A. J. LAWRENCE, Esq, C.I.E.
LADY HOWSE	MRS F. LUCAS
SIR F. WIGAN	MRS TREVELYAN MARTIN
LADY WILLS	MRS MUMFORD
MRS CHARLES BARCLAY	F. H. NORMAN, Esq
A. BEIT, Esq	MRS LEWIN PAYNE
MRS BELLINGHAM SMITH	MRS PYE-SMITH
J. H. BEYNON, Esq	L. E. SHAW, Esq, M.D.
MRS BEYNON	MRS SHAW-STEWART
MISS ELLA BONSOR	MRS T. G. STEVENS
MRS BRAILEY	MRS SYMONDS
F. W. DEACON	MRS TARGETT
T. DEBENHAM, Esq	MRS F. TAYLOR
L. A. DUNN, Esq, M. S.	E. L. WALFORD, Esq
MRS FAWCETT	

Some of the first Patrons and Patronesses

The Countess of Bective

The Hon Arthur J. Balfour

Sir Alfred Fripp

There were also many Patrons and Patronesses who were drawn from the good and the great of the time; Viscounts and Countesses, Lords and Ladies, and MPs. These could be admitted onto the Council as associates on paying an annual subscription of one guinea or life membership of ten guineas.

A number of the Hospital Consultants were included in the Patrons but they were outnumbered by their wives and this trend was to continue for many years to come.

Later they were renamed Honorary members and as such, they have continued to make a significant and valued contribution to the League over the years.

The structure of the Guy's League sparked some controversy. The criticism came via the pages of the British Journal of Nursing and from the pen of Mrs Bedford Fenwick. She wrote:

> 'It will be seen that Guy's Nurses' League differs from others already in existence [there were very few at that time] in that it is not entirely a self governing body of nurses, but is in reality more of a Hospital League'[11]

She was critical that the President & Chairman and some of the Council members were not nurses and was scathing about the idea of patronage.

She did concede, however, that nurses were in the majority on the Council.

Sarah Swift maintained a dignified public silence towards this dis-approval. She was no shrinking violet and would not be cowed by Hospital Administrators or Consultant medical staff. It seems that she took the pragmatic approach and one that was probably advantageous to the League at that time. It could be that she felt the League would be more powerful and successful with the full participation of the Hospital management, and the financial and other support of the Patrons.

The whole process was democratic, the League being under the control of the Council, where nurses were in the majority, with no decisions being made without at least two thirds of members voting.

Initially there were two classes of League members; Associates who were nurses in training and Life members who had completed their training and been awarded a hospital certificate.

It was compulsory for associates and life members who continued to work at Guy's to join the League and pay an annual subscription. The associates paid 5s – 15s depending on their year of training and the life members 15s. Sisters paid a guinea. Past nurses could pay an entrance fee of 2s. 6d. and an annual subscription of 2s. 6d.

The fact that Guy's nurses in training were compelled to join the League, again caused comment by Mrs Bedford Fenwick in the British Journal of Nursing.

She writes on Feb 4th 1905:

> 'We have only to state . . . that each nurse of whatever rank is compelled to join and subscribe from 5s to £1. 1s, annually to the [Guy's] Nurses' League, all liberty of action being denied the nursing staff in these matters. This bureaucratic government is quite out of date, and would not for a moment be tolerated by nurses trained in schools where entire liberty of action in such personal affairs is a matter of course'.[12]

At least one Guy's Head Nurse disagreed and wrote to the British Journal of Nursing:

> 'Your remarks about the [Guy's] Nurses' League surprise me, as from your Journal, I have always gathered that you advocated them, and they cannot be carried out without regular subscriptions, which every candidate knows before entering the hospital, she will have to pay . . . This League gives us many things – a cottage at Honor Oak, where we can spend our weekends, half days and three hours [off], with a tennis court, bicycles, etc, and a large library, debating and photographic societies, swimming club etc. In other ways the nurses here have much more liberty in every way than those in many other large London hospitals. I have spent five years in another one, and have friends in most of the others, so can speak from experience, and I may say that the liberty allowed the nurses here was a revelation to me when I first entered for training'.[13]

The membership benefits at the founding of the League were:

- *To have her name and address inserted in each new edition of the register.*
- *To receive periodical editions of the register.*
- *To have particulars of former appointments and any change of work or appointment inserted in the register.*

- *To make use of the grounds of the League at Honor Oak Park, and to participate in the privileges of all sections of the League, subject to such restrictions as the Council may find it necessary to impose.*
- *To be informed as far as possible of matters of interest taking place at the Hospital, and to receive an invitation to attend the annual general meeting of the League.*[14]

The Guy's Nurses' League immediately became an integral part of the nursing scene at Guy's. League members represented the hospital in national forums and the clubs and societies continued to thrive. The annual AGMs brought Guy's nurses back together, and the register enabled them to maintain links with their friends and colleagues throughout the world.

CHAPTER THREE

The Clubs and Societies

W hen the League was formed it incorporated the Choral Society, the Cycling Club, the Lawn Tennis & Croquet Club, and the Library.

Some of these organisations were to play a part in League activities for many years to come and were joined later by the Debating Society, the Swimming Club, the Photographic society, the Needlework section, the Dramatic society, the Gardening Club and the Hockey club. Representatives of the clubs sat on the League Council, each one being represented by a sister and a nurse, who were elected or re-elected annually.

In 1891 Guy's had purchased land in Honor Oak Park as a sports ground and an area was identified here for Lawn Tennis Courts and a Croquet Lawn for the nurses. Honor Oak Park, which is near Lewisham, in London, was, at that time, almost a rural area and therefore thought to be a safe place for the nurses to cycle.

The Recreation Society had approached the House Committee for money to acquire this land and for the building of a pavilion. The Committee granted £3,909 6s. 11d. on the condition that the League paid an annual rent of 3%. This was sufficient funding to level and fence the land, to provide two tennis courts and a croquet lawn, a shady garden and to build a Club House, thereafter referred to as 'The Cottage'.

The Cottage

The original Cottage had rooms for resident caretakers, a large tea room, two bedrooms for nurses and a large bicycle stable which was converted into two more double bedrooms for the nurses in 1906.

The Cottage

The Cottage was to act as a club house and sanctuary for League members for the next forty years. Nurses would spend a weekend there or visit for a few hours when not working. It was said that, particularly in the early days, the cottage and grounds allowed a freedom for single women normally denied to them by the conventions of the time.

The number of weekend and 'short visits' was reported at each AGM. In 1910, 146 sisters and nurses had spent weekends and nights at the Cottage and 700 shorter visits for tea had been made and by 1914 weekends had risen to 170 and short visits to 1,252.

During the first world war the cottage was closed for a while but re-opened in May 1918.

In 1919 two of the Governors, Lord Revelstoke and Sir Cosmo Bonsor, donated £3,000 for a memorial to the work done by Guy's nurses during the war. On the suggestion of The Matron, Margaret Hogg, it was spent on enlarging the Cottage and improving the garden. This then provided sleeping accommodation for twelve nurses. In 1920 the League held a garden party at the Cottage at which Lord Revelstoke performed the opening ceremony. He rang the doorbell and the door was opened by Miss Hogg who bade him welcome on behalf of all Guy's nurses. He then stepped in and declared the upgraded Cottage 'open'.

From time to time the League had paid money off the capital sum originally borrowed from the hospital and by 1923, the League's debt had been reduced to £894. The League Council decided to try and raise funds to pay off the debt and £298 had been raised towards it when Sir Cosmo Bonsor intervened and brought the future ownership of the Cottage before the Governors. It was found that as the League was not a Corporate Body it could not hold freehold property so the Governors granted a 999 year lease to the Trustees (the President of the League, the Matron and the Hospital Superintendent) to hold the cottage and grounds in trust for the League. This meant the League had possession and control of the property subject to an annual payment of £27 in rent.

The Cottage continued to be a popular destination for the nurses throughout the 1920s but during the 1930s the use decreased as other options for leisure activities became available to them. In 1936, an increase in the nursing establishment meant a further demand on the nurses' home at Guy's so the League allowed the Governors to rent some rooms for nursing accommodation at the Cottage.

Matron Emily MacManus was very fond of the Cottage and initiated a League re-union Garden Party there in 1929. The event was advertised in the Nursing Press and about 150 past and present nurses attended.

During the afternoon a band played delightful music, receiving many encores, and, after tea, which was served on the lawn, tennis, clock golf and other games engaged the attention of the guests, and a very happy afternoon came to an end all too soon.

The Garden party at the Cottage became a regular event until WW2. At the outbreak of war a Barrage Balloon was sited in the grounds and later local residents were given permission to dig up part of the garden for allotments.

In 1944, Miss MacManus, distressed to learn that the Cottage had been damaged by several bombs, wrote:

> 'the current nurses in training know nothing of the Cottage, although I am looking forward to the time, when war has ceased and the League can hold a wonderful re-union there and the Cottage and grounds will be restored to their former beauty and usefulness. It would be good if some past Guy's Nurses with time to spare would band together to help the Matron by taking the garden and the house under their wing and slowly bring order out of chaos'.[15]

However, sadly, this was not to be. Times had changed and the Cottage was now in a built up area. Although the tennis courts were re-laid and there were other inducements to attract the nurses back, it had ceased to appeal to them and in December 1948 the Cottage was closed. It was sold in 1949 for a net profit of £4,875 which the Governors most generously allowed the League to keep. The Cottage was eventually demolished to make way for housing in the 1960s.

The Cottage early 1900s

The Sports Clubs

The tennis and swimming clubs were the most successful and long lasting of the sporting clubs. The Cycling Club, formed in 1896, was also very popular but short lived when in 1911 it was decided that the increase in motor traffic made cycling in London too dangerous!

The Lawn Tennis club

Lawn tennis became a popular sport for middle class Victorian women towards the end of the 19th century. At Guy's in 1894, the nurses began to enjoy tennis when they were allowed to use the medical student's tennis courts three times a week. The nurses' Lawn Tennis and Croquet Club was formed in 1896.

Edwardian ladies had to play wearing ankle length skirts with a long sleeve blouse; not at all conducive to ease of movement.

The League club rules stated that, when playing, members must wear tennis shoes without heels – presumably saving a few sprained ankles.

The first recorded success for the tennis club was the winning of the inaugural Nursing Times Lawn Tennis Challenge Cup

Edwardian lady tennis player

for nurses in 1912. The final was played against the Central London Sick Asylum at the Edmonton Infirmary, in front of a crowd of about 100. The Guy's Hospital 'A' team was Sister Stewart and Nurse Raven and they won 6–1, 6–2, 6–1. The 'B' team of Nurse Maher and Nurse Hodgkinson defeated the CLSA 'B' team 6–3, 6–1, 6–3.

A game in progress

The Guy's winning team on the left; standing: Nurses Maher & Hodgkinson, seated: Nurse Raven and Sister Stewart

When the victorious team returned to Guy's the cup was carried into the Sisters' dining room while they were having dinner. It was placed on a table amid loud cheers before being taken to its final place in the nurses' dining room.

The Honorary Secretary of the Lawn Tennis Club declared that it was a splendid thing for the nurses, who had thoroughly enjoyed the games, and had played much more tennis this year than ever before. The members of the team were delighted with their little silver replicas of the cup.

Nurse Maher was later to be appointed as Sister on Astley Cooper and remained as the tennis representative on Council until 1920.

The Nursing Times Lawn Tennis Challenge Cup

Guy's continued to have success in the inter-hospitals tournament for over 60 years. In 1978 the doubles tournament was won by Jane Fox and Rosalind Arkell and this then meant that Guy's had won this trophy more than any other hospital.

In the 1960s the expansion of the hospital increased pressure on space and the tennis courts at Guys were built on.

Despite this tennis continued to thrive until the 1980s when interest waned not just at Guy's but all the London Hospitals and the inter-hospitals tournament ended.

Ladies doubles tennis players

The Swimming Club

Sir Henry Raphael generously donated 20,000 to build a nurses' home in memory of his wife Henriette and other members of the Raphael family had given money for a swimming pool in the basement. The Henriette Raphael Nurses Home was opened by the Prince & Princess of Wales in 1902.

In an article about the new nurses' home in the British Journal of Nursing of July 5th 1902 the swimming pool is described thus:

> '[H]ere is a noble swimming-bath . . . It is shallow at one end and gradually increases in depth. The water is kept at a warm temperature. The walls of this great room, of which the floor space is occupied by the bath, are white and green, and a cooler, pleasanter place on a hot summer's day it would be difficult to imagine. There is little doubt that the nurses will revel in their swimming-bath and will gain both in health and pleasure from the kindly provision made for them'.[16]

The swimming pool was an immediate hit with the nursing staff and was used extensively although competitive swimming for women was not permitted for several more years. (Women were first allowed to take part in swimming at the Olympic Games in 1912).

The nurses admire their swimming pool

Emily MacManus, later Matron of Guy's, told a story about her exploits in the pool when she was a student nurse. At a swimming gala she entered for an illustrated advertisements race and she went as a rather large cook advertising soup. In the advert the cook held a large tureen with the inscription 'My Dear, buy it'.

Emily borrowed a large soup tureen from the nurses' home and dressed appropriately, walked out onto the diving board, made a bow and dived in.

She won the competition but abandoned the tureen which sank to the bottom of the pool. Later that evening an irate head dining room maid met Emily and demanded the return of the tureen. After much difficulty and by kicking it underwater from the deep to the shallow end, Emily managed to retrieve it.[17]

After WW1 in 1920 the club was reported to have held a very successful swimming drama. The prettiest event was the candle race, held in the darkness, and won by Nurse Dudfield, who swam two lengths of the bath with her candle unextinguished.

1922 saw the first report of the club taking part in the inter-hospitals competition. The Guy's team won a handsome silver challenge cup presented by Sir Alfred & Lady Fripp, and they won this for the next 4 years. This cup was still being competed for in the 1950s.

The swimming club continued to be successful and in 1949 won the Nursing Mirror Pre-Eminent Shield for the best team at the event.

The swimming club continued to be successful throughout the 80s and the 90s and was supported by the League until 2003.

Over the years The League did much to sponsor and support the swimming club, purchasing costumes, caps, paying for training etc. This generosity was partly returned in 1996 when the Swimming Team took place in a Charity Gala which raised £420 and requested that £250 of it be donated to the Guy's Nurses' League.

1949 Winning Team

This cup was won again in 1960 and later in 1985.

*1985 Winning team Paul Hughes, David Bone, Jeffery Edmunds, Ian Black,
Charlotte Berry, Hilary Winter, Jo Christian, Jo Harvey, Kim Britt Hodger,
Sheena Pollock, Julia Cave (Captain)*

The Cycling Club

In the 1890s cycling had become a very popular pastime for both sexes
and in 1895 the Guy's Hospital Nurses' Cycling Club was formed.
Bicycles were hired to club members at 1d. a day but only after they had
been passed as fit to ride by an instructor. The club uniform, which was
compulsory, was a long blue serge skirt and jacket with a blue blouse and
black or white sailor hat with a black band or one in Guy's colours.

A cottage in Lewisham called 'The Limes' was found to act as a club
house; although, soon after, this was moved to 'The Cottage' in Honor
Oak Park. This area was then an almost rural environment and it was
thought to be a safe place for the nurses to cycle.

The cycling club was enjoyed by many Guy's nurses until it was
disbanded in 1911 for safety reasons.

Edwardian lady cyclist

The British Journal of Nursing was impressed by the formation of the club at Guy's and published the following article in 1896.

Nurses and Cycling   British Journal of Nursing 1896

'In these days of universal wheeling, when every other person one meets is either a confirmed devotee of the wheel, or an embryo in the throes of learning the fascinating pastime, the example set by Guy's Hospital in founding the Nurses' Cycling Club is one that may well be imitated by others of our great centres of 'healing art'. The authorities that be of the noble monument of the 'pious founder' have inaugurated this club by hiring a cottage in a district but a short distance from town, where the Sisters and Nurses can keep their machines, together with the necessary change of clothes. Thus, within half an hour, the members of one of the most useful and at the same time, most trying, professions open to women, will have the opportunity of finding themselves transplanted from their customary surroundings of pain and suffering into the country, with all its advantages of free breathing space, and unlimited expanse of heaven. For those who cannot afford to buy their own machines, subscriptions are invited to stock a few at the little club house, in order that the less fortunate ones may share the evident advantages which might otherwise be denied them.

To those acquainted in any way with the lives of the 'workers in wards', the proposal plan can but appeal in the very strongest light. None but the initiated can, perhaps, realize the terrible strain on the nerves, engendered by the daily, and even hourly, continuous watching over and caring for the maimed, the sick, and the halt. Mr Gladstone once remarked that 'all time and money spent in training the body pays a larger interest than any other investment', and in the case of Nursing Staff of our large Hospitals, both in town and in the country, leading, as they do in many cases, lives of anxiety and monotony, the charitable public of the richest empire in the world could not better invest a trifle. By doing so, they will be granting the means whereby those who devote so much of their own health and energies to the alleviation of suffering, may have the opportunity of indulging in a form of recreation which thousands of human beings have found of estimable benefit in aiding them to fulfil their daily duties in life.

Though medical men are found to condemn the practice for those of the weaker sex, the generality of doctors not only are wheelmen themselves, but permit and encourage their wives and daughters to take advantage of a means of locomotion which offers unlimited opportunities for seeing the world at a small cost. Like every other form of exercise, great discretion must be used with regard to the amount of cycling suitable to each individual rider. As, however, nearly all the large Hospitals in London now have 'Gazettes' published by their medical schools, in which such questions as the 'Medical Aspects of Cycling' and so on, are discussed by our leading physicians and surgeons, Nurses have far more opportunities of learning the gentle art of self restraint, than the outside public. It is but natural that this popular and exhilarating exercise should find its detractors, but we doubt if even the following words, 'The "poets ideal" of exquisite womanhood is utterly destroyed by the sight of these perspiring, red-faced lank haired objects working their legs treadmill fashion, and tearing along every road in the country', written by the gifted Marie Corelli, will in any way act as a deterrent to a class of woman who may justify claim very near relationship with the poet's ideal. To those of us who can appreciate the blessings of any form of muscular recreation, a feeling of sadness can but be caused by seeing one of such undoubted talents as the writer whose words we have quoted, using her great influence against healthy indoor exercise for her sex. We can but hope that the initiative of 'Guy's' may cause a healthy spirit of rivalry to be engendered in the breasts of those responsible for the physical welfare of the Nurses of many another similar institution, both in London and in the provinces, and that the British public will do their best to aid in the proposed amelioration of the lot of those who, if they do not find that 'the roughest road often leads to the smoothest fortune' may yet surmount many a rough road leading to the restoration of strength and energy'.[18]

The Leisure Societies

The Library

The Library was founded by Miss Lilian Tippetts in 1898, when she was a Staff Nurse at Guy's. She became a League member when it was founded in 1900 and by this time had been promoted to Sister. The Library was well used by the League members with thousands of books being loaned each year. There were novels as well as medical books and member's suggestions for new books could be submitted to Council. The League gave an annual subscription to maintain the library and provide new books.

In 1962 the Fiction Library was moved to a new facility in the School of Nursing.

In 1972 as the nurses' use of the Fiction Library had greatly reduced, the League decided to discontinue the annual subscription. The Library was gradually phased out, although the larger reference tomes remained in the Hilda Gration Room.

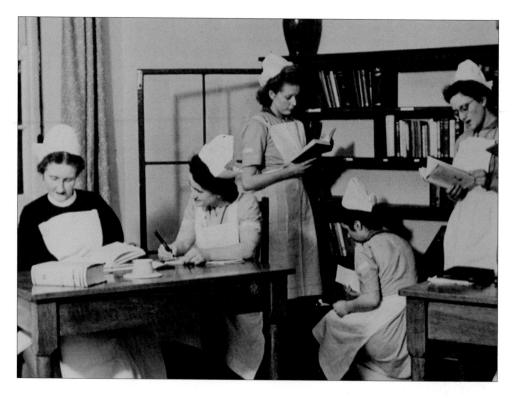

The Nurses' Library

The Nurses' Choral Society (later the Music Society)

Founded in 1895 the Choral Society was an immediate success giving regular concerts and providing entertainment at the AGMs and other events.

As early as November 1900, Matron Esther Young had agreed that the Nurses' Choral Society could rehearse with the Medical Students 'Glee Club' and in December 1902 they held their first joint concert with proceeds going to League Funds.

In 1906, an orchestra was formed and it was suggested that the Choral Society, the Glee Club and the Orchestra be combined to form the Guy's Hospital Musical Society.

The Society continued to thrive, giving regular concerts, with Gilbert & Sullivan being a particular favourite. The Christmas Concert, often held in Southwark Cathedral was a popular event.

The Music Society was suspended during the second world war and not re-formed until 1955 when Joy Jordan (née Strut) came to undertake her nurse training at Guy's. On arrival she expected to be able to join an active music club but was disappointed to find no club at all.

A talented musician and singer herself she was determined to do something about it and she started a Nurses' Choir. Later she met two medical students, Bob Sells and Dick Strickland, who were also interested in music and they decided to form a mixed choir and orchestra. This developed into the music club which continues today as the thriving GKT (Guy's, King's & St Thomas') Music Society, open to all staff and students.

The League continued to support the Music Society into the 1990s, giving them an annual grant of £150 and frequently funding concerts and performances.

The Music Society

From 1969 for the next thirty years, League members and colleagues sang at the Sir Malcolm Sergeant Carol concerts held at the Royal Festival Hall and later the Albert Hall.

The Guy's Choir join many other hospital choirs at the Royal Festival Hall

The Debating Society

Towards the end of the nineteenth century, debating societies for women were becoming popular. The Guy's Hospital Nurses' debating society, formed in 1904, was not immediately successful. Young ladies at that time were not used to publically expressing their views to others and perhaps they were a little intimidated by the presence of Matron Sarah Swift who was the Society President and had the power of veto.

However by 1911 it had taken on a new lease of life. Matron, Miss Haughton reported at the AGM that there had been three spirited debates during the year. She also said that she was not allowed to attend the meetings which may have been the secret of the society's increased popularity. Subjects for debate were suggested by the members and were alternately nursing matters and general subjects.

In 1912 the main interest of discussion was women's suffrage and the members had excellent addresses from Mrs Helena Swanwick and Miss Maude Royden, both well known Suffragettes. This led to the formation of a Hospital Suffrage society called The Tabard in 1913.

The debating society did not meet during WW1 but was revived in the 1920s. In 1928, Dorothy Holland, later to be Senior Sister Tutor, was voted onto Council as the Debating Society Representative, and she did much to revive it.

The subject for debate that year was 'Marriage versus Career'. At the close of the debate 'Marriage' was carried by a large majority.

The following year the topic debated was 'Is popularity a test of merit?' – this was voted against by a large majority. In the same year a debate was held for the night nurses, speeches being limited to two minutes on topics suggested from the floor. One on 'Long versus short skirts' caused great merriment and another 'Is suicide ever justifiable', great interest.

In 1932 the topics were 'A jack of all trades is better than a master of one', 'The World does not progress it merely changes' and 'In the interests of progress of the country the Cinema should be discouraged'. All these motions were lost.

The society was suspended during WW2 and was not reformed after the war.

The Photographic Society

This was formed in 1905 and was affiliated with the Royal Photographic Society of Great Britain. The society's aims were the promotion of photographic knowledge by means of lectures, discussions and practical demonstrations, and it committed to an annual exhibition of prints and slides.

A dark room was provided for the use of members. The society was an immediate success and held its first exhibition in 1906 at the AGM. In 1907 there were no less than 210 entries, three of which were printed in the Nursing Mirror.

Apart from the two world wars a photographic exhibition was held every year, the skill of the photographers and standard of the entries receiving much praise. In the early days many entries were sent by members from far flung parts of the world from Corsica to Canada and South Africa to Srinagar.

The Matron and Sister,
Kandy Hospital
(*Taken by Miss Wilkinson*)

Tea-Time at Chelsea Royal Hospital
(*Taken by Miss Smith, 2nd Prize*)

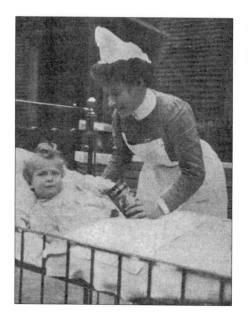

"Ah! Sweeties"
(*Taken by Miss Smith*)

Reproduced from Nursing Mirror, 1907

Prizes were awarded in a number of different classes; in 1913 Sister Addison received the prize for best picture in the exhibition for her charming study in sea and cloud. Her photos were taken with a Number 2 Brownie which, it was said, proved that an expensive camera was not necessary to produce good work.

During the 1950s interest declined, fewer entries were received and the last exhibition was held in 1958.

Associated Societies

The following were not included in the League constitution but were very much part of League activities and warranted a representative on Council.

Needlework

Sewing and embroidery had long been a leisure pursuit for young ladies and it was decided that a needlework exhibition should be included at the 1913 AGM.

Classes were held and many entries were received including: darning, crochet, plain needlework, white embroidery, lace, drawn thread work, and hardanger work. An exhibition of needlework joined photography as a permanent feature of every AGM until 1959, and from 1917 onwards a needlework representative was voted on to the League council.

The first exhibition was described as being:

> . . . 'so excellent that there was no doubt that it had come to stay.

> . . . The delicacy of the lace, the daintiness of the needlework, the beauty of the Hardanger drawn thread work, proved abundantly that though fine needlework may be in some danger of becoming a lost art in these hustling days, skill in its fashioning still lingers in the fingertips of Guy's nurses'.[19]

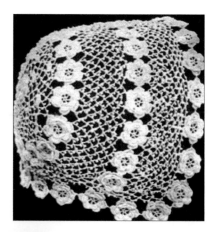

Some examples of Edwardian needlework

The Dramatic Society

The first account of the nurses 'performing' was in 1905 when they gave a Christmas entertainment; the day nurses providing the first half and the night nurses the second. The Christmas entertainments continued each year and gave the nurses the opportunity to show off their talents and let their hair down.

Entertainment also brought medical and nursing staff together to enjoy themselves in an unprecedented way.

In 1907 the nurses put on a public show for the first time without the help of the medical staff. The farces, songs, dances and tableaux were warmly received. One of the most popular was 'The Light Brigade' when a dozen nurses with Sister Ida at their head appeared on the stage wearing tiny electric arcs on their breast and sang the praises of the 'Light Department' (later re-named the x-ray department). Equally well received was 'Nurses, Past, Present, and Future' which forecast a coming 'race' of graduate nurses in cap and gown, to whom the present curriculum will appear elementary and outdated and who will thank goodness that times have changed. This was very prophetic but not realised for almost another century!

The Dramatic Society in the 1920s

During WW2 League members turned to pantomime. In 1943 when part of Guy's had been transferred to Orpington the nurses put on Dick Whittington with League member Esme Few as the Principal Boy. (*opposite*)

Esme Few

In 1995 the idea of pantomime was revived when the then Chairman of the League, Betsy Morley, with other League members decided to put on a pantomime to revive morale at Guy's following the decision to move all acute services to St Thomas' Hospital.

The first performance, in January 1996 was Little Red Riding Hood or Who's Afraid of Virginia Wolff (Virginia Bottomley, was a Conservative Politician at the time, and had been Secretary of State for Health). All the jokes were political in nature with a heavy emphasis on the decisions regarding the changes at Guy's. What was planned as a one-off product-ion, became an annual event for the next fourteen years, culminating with Sleeping Beauty in 2008, described as the best ever.

Betsy was the writer, director and producer of the pantomimes while other League members made important contributions with Lisa Burnapp as the wardrobe mistress, Gill Moore as the Stage Manager and Joy Kimberely as the Artistic Director.

These pantomimes brought all levels of staff together, from executive directors, nurses, doctors, pharmacists, secretaries, porters and many more.

The Cast of Robin Hood

Artistic Director Joy Kimberley with one of her creations for Robinson Crusoe

League ex-Chairman Lisa Burnapp playing the part of 'SeaQueen' the good fairy in Robinson Crusoe with Amelia Silas, the daughter of another League member, as her assistant, 'Hebe'

CHAPTER FOUR

The Annual General Meetings and Council

The Annual General Meetings (AGMS) and the Council meetings have managed League affairs since its formation in 1902.

The AGMs

The AGMs, as well as being the formal occasion when accounts were presented and Council election results announced, were also a focus for League members to return to Guy's to be re-united with their friends and colleagues.

The agenda has changed very little throughout the life of the League and as well as the financial accounts have included League and Hospital news, reports from the sports and leisure clubs, news of the membership and in later years reports from the Editor of the League Journal and the Secretaries of the Benevolent and Scholarship funds.

Occasionally at the AGM a vote would be taken on a specific issue though most decision making was made by Council.

One hundred years ago, Leagues were regarded as important nursing institutions and their activities were reported in detail in the national nursing press of the day. The Guy's AGM was a grand affair, presided over by the Matron, as Honorary Secretary. In 1909 the British Journal of Nursing reflected on the Guy's League AGM:

> *'Of the success of this new movement there can be little doubt, everyone appreciating the opportunity of exchanging views, ideas, and thoughts,*

the members, some of whom now hold responsible posts as Matrons of important hospitals, talking of the times when they were trained under less luxurious circumstances . . . Thus was spent a very pleasant and instructive evening, and much pleasure was expressed by those present at having met so many old friends, an opportunity for which so seldom presents itself, and also hope that all may meet again next year' [20]

An invited guest was asked to chair the meeting and address the members. These were usually prominent Guy's trained nurses, often an ex-Guy's Matron or the Matron of another Hospital and they spoke on a variety of topics.

In 1910 the guest chairman was Gertrude Rogers who was Matron at Leicester Infirmary. She began by saying what an honour it was to be asked to chair the Guy's AGM. She thought that maybe members were wondering why she, *'a country cousin'*,[7] had been invited to occupy the chair. She explained that she had once been Sister Clinical at Guy's though she thought that some of those present were probably in their cradles at the time.

She then spoke fondly of Matron Burt who had gone to Leicester from Guy's:

'. . . It was largely to the inspiration of Guy's that the Leicester League owed its origin, and another tie was that it was to Guy's that the Leicester Infirmary owed its first Matron, Miss Burt. When Miss Burt went to Leicester nursing was almost non existent. There were two night nurses for 200 patients, and their instructions were not to stay in any ward but to walk through them all at intervals. She had been told by a former house surgeon that the house staff used to tie the feet of the night nurses to the chairs in which they were esconsed (sleeping), to bring home to them that they had visited the wards . . .

Miss Burt was not there long, but she left Leicester with a well organised school when she returned to Guy's.

'Miss Burt', said Miss Rogers, *'was a reformer. She was not popular – reformers who get people out of their armchairs, rarely are: but she fought a good fight and won the victory for you. I think if she could come back now she would find the victory worth while, and would not grudge the time and labour she spent in organising the Training School. I am sorry she cannot see the fruit of her work.'* [21]

In 1914 Margaret Atkey, Matron of the County Hospital, Newport was the guest speaker. She had trained at Guy's from 1901–04 and had held a Sister's post there from 1905–08. She spoke of the importance of the Guy's League.

> '. . . When it was founded it was before the times, now everyone was talking of Leagues. Past members of the League, working far away in country posts, are glad to read of its doings in the nursing press. She reminded those present that in their endeavour to keep ahead of things they must realise, as it is right they should, their duty to their profession as a whole, but they should also not leave behind the fine traditions of the older nurses, who were devoted to their patients . . .'[22]

After WW1 in 1920, Miss Constance Todd, Royal Red Cross 1st Class and holder of the Military Medal, who had been Matron of the St John's Ambulance Brigade Hospital in Etaples, France during the war was the guest chairman. The hospitals in Etaples were notoriously bombed by German planes and she told an amusing tale of a German pilot who was shot down and having been brought to the hospital, loudly demanded he be sent to England so that he would not be bombed by his compatriots! Miss Todd, later to be Mrs Chilman, trained at Guy's from 1903–07.

In 1918, the meeting was chaired by Miss Lucy Jolley who said:

> She was quite unable to resist the temptation of accepting the invitation as 'dear old Guy's' was a magnetic attraction to her. Having had the privilege of nursing the sick and wounded at the front, the sacred duty of it was specially borne in up on her, and she appealed to her hearers to keep up the high standards and ideals of good nursing. The College of Nursing Co Ltd., after strenuous work is now fully established. We were glad to hear a generous allusion to the work for State Registration 'which' said Miss Jolley has been so long and faithfully worked for and this must come . . .'
>
> 'War has taught us that union is strength. Let us work together for the common good and put the profession on a firm and sound foundation'.[23]

Miss Jolley, returned to chair the AGM in 1922 as the Lady Superintendent of Holloway Prison. She trained at Guy's from 1903–06 and had been a Night Sister and later a Holiday Sister there as well as working in the Preliminary Training School. She had a distinguished war record, as a

Sister in the Queen Alexandra Imperial Military Nursing Service Reserve (Q.A.I.M.N.S.R) and went to France with the British Expeditionary Force in 1914. Later she was Assistant Matron and then Matron in Chief of the Royal Air Force Nursing Service.

She received a Royal Red Cross medal and was mentioned in despatches.

She spoke of her work at Holloway:

> 'By no means were they all really bad characters. Some seemed to come in from sheer bad luck, others had weak wills, and had much good in them if they would keep away from silly companions, others again got into trouble through their uncontrollable tempers.
>
> Some people thought that nurses were wasted in prisons but this was far from being the case. Many of the prisoners were feeble minded or suffered from mental deficiency or epilepsy.
>
> Some women preferred to be in prison: one who was discharged at midday was knocking at the gate by the same evening begging to be taken back in. Another woman deliberately broke a chemist's shop window so she would be taken back to Holloway'.[24]

The Guy's League AGMs were very popular, with members travelling from all over the country to be there, so in 1909 it was decided to provide a dinner for those attending. The first dinner was hosted by Sarah Swift, and took place before the meeting. It was a great success and thereafter became an annual event.

The dinner of 1911 was reported in the British Journal of Nursing:

> 'The Guy's Hospital Past and Present Nurses' League had a most successful meeting on Friday, 28th April, when, according to their custom, the members dined together in the spacious and beautiful dining room of the Nurses' Home. Miss Swift, (the late Matron), presided at the dinner, and Sisters took the head of the many tables, everything being so well organised, and the service so expeditious, that the large number present were quickly served. Dinner was a most pleasant and informal meal, and as usual when the former nurses of a training school meet once more, the warm greetings were many, and the conversation never flagged'.[25]

At the same meeting the iconic portrait of Sarah Swift by Henry Draper, depicted on page 14, was presented to the League by an anonymous donor. The picture was not on display as the artist had taken it to try and get it hung in the Royal Academy.

The dinners continued during the first world war despite the hardships and reduced numbers.

After the war numbers increased again, with a record attendance in 1920 when tickets sold out and people were turned away.

In 1923 over 200 members attended and the event was described thus:

> *The room looked very charming, freshly decorated in duck egg blue and brown; and on the tables at which the Sisters presided, vases of lovely yellow tulips, flanked with lemonade, made a charmingly gay decoration. We wish the Home Sister would divulge the secret of how to provide an excellent four-course dinner, followed by coffee, at a shilling a head. Many Leagues would like to know; and she would add to their indebtedness if she included the recipe for that novel and excellent sweet named 'Abbot's Delight'.*[26]

The tradition of the annual dinner continues to this day.

League members enjoy the Annual Dinner in the Robens Suite at Guy's in 2005

The annual nurses' prize giving also took place during the AGM. In 1925 the medals for 1924 were presented by Sir Cosmo Bonsor.

The Butterworth medal: instituted by Joshua W Butterworth in 1889, is awarded to all nurses of Guy's Hospital who shall have completed 5 years continuous satisfactory service at the said Hospital and was given to Sisters Edith M Bodkin, Evelyn M Cawthorne, Alice E Cornwall, Evelyn M Elliot, Mary E Jameson, Frances L Mutimer, Amy T Samuel and Florence J Smith.

The Casenove Medal: awarded to the nurse who shall have obtained the highest aggregate percentage of marks in all the Examinations held during 1923–24 was shared by Gladys Ireland and Norah Kersley who had achieved the same marks.

The Butterworth Medal presented to Norah Dickinson, Student Nurse 1925–29 and Staff Nurse/Sister 1929–32

The Casenove Medal presented to Harriet Boulay in 1902

The Keogh Prize: consisting of surgical instruments, awarded to the nurse obtaining the highest marks in the Surgery Examinations, went to Mary Isaac.

The Morrison Prizes: which were medical books were awarded to Gladys Bloomfield and Phyllis Carden for the highest marks in Medicine and Nursing subjects.

The Governors Prizes which were also medical books and were awarded to Probationers obtaining the highest marks in the two junior examinations again went to Phyllis Carden and to Muriel Alchin.[27]

In 1947 the nurses' prize giving became a separate event although the Butterworth medals continued to be presented at the League AGM.

The AGMs had always been held on a Friday evening but in 1940 the meeting was moved to the afternoon due to blackout regulations. In 1951 members were asked to vote for a change of day for the meeting from Friday to Saturday.

In 1958, Emily MacManus became President of the League and it was decided to ask her to chair the AGM, and from 1966 onwards it became the tradition that the AGM was chaired by the League President.

A guest speaker continued to be part of the proceedings and during the 1980s there was a succession of distinguished Guy's Consultants invited to present the Butterworth medals and address the meeting.

Their remit must have been to entertain their audience and take them down memory lane, for as reported in the Journals at the time:

In 1979 Mr Salmon gave an *'amusing address'*.

In 1980 Dr MacLean gave an *'amusing and interesting address'*.

In 1981 Professor Keith Simpson gave an *'amusing and absorbing address recalling the many Guy's personalities he had known and his own experiences during his 57 years at Guy's'*.

In 1982 Dr Stafford-Clark gave an *'interesting and amusing address recalling his time at Guy's both as a medical student and a doctor'*.

In 1983 Mr T. Lewis proceeded to deliver a *'colourful and entertaining series of personal reminiscences of life at Guy's since 1939'*.

In 1984 Dr Robert Knight spoke in reminiscing mood delighting members with *'amusing anecdotes which had occurred during his student days and work at Guy's'*.

Sadly there are no records of these stories and anecdotes until 1985 when Professor Cyril Chantler's talk was recorded in the Journal. He spoke of his respect for Guy's nurses created by both affection and fear. One of his anecdotes concerned his first week as a ward clerk (medical student) on the wards:

'In those days syringes were made of glass, plungers for the syringes were often inadequately greased and the needles had been used many times before. My trepidation at my first venepuncture was matched by the fortitude of the patient, who gave me much useful advice as I attempted to spear his vein rather like a matador fighting his first bull.

Eventually I was successful and overcome with elation I pulled on the plunger until it fell out of the end and 10cc of blood spilt over the sheets. 'Don't turn round' said the unfortunate victim, 'but I think you're in deep trouble lad' And I was, because the lady in blue [the ward Sister] *was standing behind me.*[28]

Clockwise from top left: Dr David Stafford-Clark; Professor Keith Simpson; Dr Bob Knight and Professor Sir Cyril Chantler all of whom entertained League members at AGMs in the 1980s

The speakers in the following years covered many varied and interesting subjects but it was not until 2009 at the penultimate AGM that a Guy's Consultant, Mike O'Brien returned to reminisce with the members. Dr O'Brien gave a presentation of slides of 50 years of Guy's history, which included many familiar faces of past League and Hospital personalities.

League members listening intently to the guest speaker at the AGM in 2007

The AGM first took place in the nurses' recreation room in the Henriette Raphael Nurses Home and around 170 members attended. Following meetings took place in the Nurses Sitting room and an average of 200 members attended each year.

In 1929, due to the increase in numbers of members attending, the meeting was moved to the gymnasium of the massage department (massage was the fore-runner of Physiotherapy) and the following year even greater numbers meant another move to the Outpatient Department.

By the 1950s the AGM was held in the Physiology Theatre in the Medical School. In 1962 due to overcrowding at this venue, the Matron wrote to the Clerk to the Governors expressing the concern of the League Council that there was no suitable accommodation for the League AGM

The Nurses Sitting Room

One of the panoramic views of London from the Robens Suite

and suggesting that any future building plans, include a large Assembly Hall for functions and large gatherings.

Despite the pressure on the venue, the meeting continued here until 1976, and in 1965 there was a record attendance of 400, helped by the provision of a crèche so that members with small children could attend.

From 1976 when the AGM coincided with the Hospital's 250th anniversary, and for several years to come, the members enjoyed the more comfortable surroundings of the newly opened Greenwood Theatre.

The final AGM's of the League took place in the Robens Suite on the 29th floor of Guy's Tower where the members were in danger of being distracted from the proceedings by the panoramic views of London. By now average attendances were 90–100.

The final AGM in 2010 saw 350 members crammed into yet another new venue, the New Hunts House Lecture theatre.

The Chapel

The re-union service in the Guy's Chapel was an important part of the AGM day as the Chapel holds a special place in the hearts of many League members.

Nurses in the Chapel

In the early days Chapel attendance was compulsory for all nurses and until the 1960s there were still daily early morning prayers in the Chapel for those who wished to attend.

An invited preacher was often asked to take the AGM service, frequently a Bishop or other high ranking Churchman.

For over 70 years at the AGM, the members remembered their colleagues, who had died during the previous twelve months, until Matron, Linda Titley, suggested that maybe this would be more appropriate at the Chapel service and this was agreed. The names were read out by the Preacher or one of the Officers, followed by a prayer. The Guy's prayer was then read by all those present.

The Guy's Prayer

Bless, O Lord, all who have gone from this place to work in many different parts of your world. Sustain them by your good Spirit in all that they undertake so that they may know, in ministering to the needs of others, they are serving you. Enable us all to grow in understanding and love so that we may come to that fullness of life which you have promised us through your Son, Jesus Christ our Lord. Amen.

The League has donated a number of items to the Chapel.

In 1964 a Festal Altar Frontal and Vestments (see previous page).

In 1973 as a memorial to Florence Taylor who had died in April 1970, the League purchased a Sanctuary Lamp for the Chapel. It was made of hand beaten silver with the Guy's crest on it and was dedicated at the AGM service. The lamp was made by David Hart, a well known silversmith who had also made the crucifix and candlesticks on the altar in the Chapel. Sadly the sanctuary lamp (insured for £1,000) was to be stolen in 1984 and was replaced by one in non precious metal but also by a silver christening bowl that would be kept in the Chapel safe.

In 1977 a carved oak Credence Table to commemorate the Queens Silver Jubilee.

A carved oak Credence Table to commemorate the Queens Silver Jubilee

League members were also responsible for many of the hassocks in the Chapel.

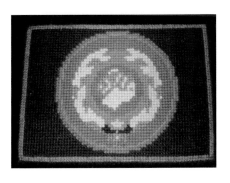 

Two well loved Matrons are also commemorated there:

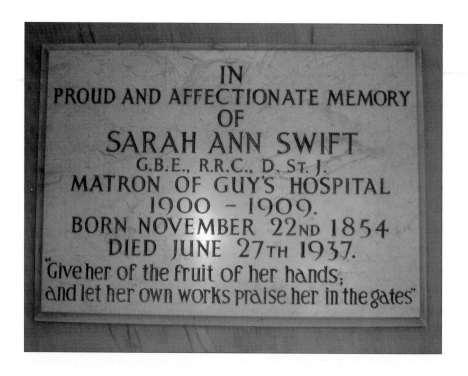

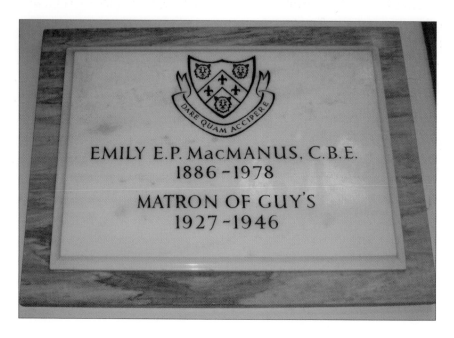

The Council

The League Council managed the affairs and finance of the League and will have met 362 times from 1900 to its closure at the end of 2010. Council members normally met four times a year. Some of their main duties included the election of Officers of Council, monitoring the finances of the League via the Honorary Treasurer, making arrangements for the AGMs and other League events and reviewing and amending the Constitution when required. For many years they also allocated the money from the Benevolent and Scholarship funds.

The Original Council

For the first twenty years the League Council was chaired by the Hospital Treasurer and for the next twenty by Lady Mabel Bonsor, who was also the President of the League.

The Medical Superintendent of the Hospital and the Honorary Secretary made up the other two ex-officio posts.

The Hospital Governors also appointed 3 or 4 other Council members.

The original Council was largely made up of representatives of the various clubs and societies, who were elected annually. There were also representatives of 'past nurses', members who no longer worked at Guy's, and these were appointed by the Council.

There were no less than nine Honorary members, who served for three years.

In 1937 the post of Assistant Honorary Secretary was added to the Council to support Matron, the Honorary Secretary, and as the League resources increased, an Executive Council comprising the League President and Honorary Secretary and the Superintendent of the Hospital, was formed to advise the Council on matters relating to property and finance.

GUY'S HOSPITAL

Past and Present Nurses' League 1903

COUNCIL 1903

Chairman:
H S COSMO. O. BONSOR, Esq.

Hon Treasurer:
Mrs J. H. BRYANT
4 St Thomas' Street,
London Bridge, S. E.

Hon Secretary:
Miss S. A. SWIFT
Matron's House,
Guy's Hospital, S. E.

Sir COOPER PERRY, M.D.
Mrs SHAW
Miss M. N. OXFORD

Past Nursing Staff Representatives:
Mrs FAGGE, 24, St Thomas' Street, S.E.
Nurse EDITH FAGGE, Guy's Institution, S.E.

Choral Representatives:
Sister LAZARUS
  (Miss R. Field)
Nurse H. DU BOURLAY

Cycling Representatives:
Sister GERTRUDE
  (Miss G. Morrah)
Nurse I. MOTT

Tennis Representatives:
Sister EDITH (Miss Lewis)
Nurse I. HILL

Library Representatives:
Sister LILIAN (Miss Tippetts)
Nurse B. WISE

Debating Representatives:
Sister ENID (Miss E. Newton)
Nurse ATKEY

Swimming Representatives:
Sister LYDIA (Miss H. Newton)
Nurse RIPLEY

Clerk to the Secretary and Treasurer:
Miss M. SMITH,
Guy's Hospital, S.E.

Mr Cosmo Bonsor – first League Council Chairman

The Council 1950s onwards

It was not until 1947 that the first nurse, Kitty Bulleid, Honorary Member, was appointed as Chairman of the Council.

Over the years as the clubs and societies closed they were no longer represented on Council. Photography and needlework ended in the 1950s although a representative for music remained until 1989, the library until 1972, tennis until 1989 and swimming until 2003.

*Sister Brysson-White, Library
Representative 1962–73*

*Penny Mawson, Music
Representative 1983–89*

The music representative was re-established in 1994 when Joan Pye was invited to sit on Council. Joan organised the League choir for the AGM and the biennial Advent Services.

From the early 1950s the Hospital Administration was no longer directly involved in the running of the League and it became much more self sufficient in managing its affairs. The Hospital Superintendent was no longer a member of the Executive Council which now comprised the League President, Chairman, Vice Chairman, Honorary Secretary & Assistant and Honorary

Joan Pye

Treasurer who were known as the Officers of the League. These met regularly to discuss issues to bring to Council and plan Council meetings.

In 1970, the League Chairman, Miss Florence Taylor, had to step down due to ill health and the Matron, Linda Titley took over. As Miss Titley lived some way from the hospital, she felt a more locally based deputy may be appropriate and she suggested that a new position of Vice Chairman be created for Florence Taylor and this then remained a permanent post on Council.

In 1975 the Constitution was changed to reflect that the Officers should serve for a period of 5 years and could not be re-elected until out of office for one year.

The President stood for a period of three years and was elected by postal vote of all members.

The Chairman of the Board remained as an ex-officio member of Council and sat on Council with other representatives of the Board of Governors until the reorganisation of the NHS in 1974, when the Board of Governors were replaced by the District Management Team.

The last Hospital Superintendent to be an ex-officio member was Dr John Helliwell who retired in 1976.

Over the next twenty years representatives of other areas of the Hospital were also invited to sit on Council, including the District Management Team, The Special Trustees (later the Charity), The School of Nursing and the Guy's & St Thomas' Trust.

In 1983, in an attempt to change the balance of Council members and get younger nurses involved, the representatives of present nursing staff were increased to nine and past representatives to six.

The difficulties in finding members to sit on Council continued and later the past and present nurse numbers were amalgamated.

In 1998/9 the League Council was re-structured after the membership of Council and tenure of the Officers had been reviewed and clarified:

- The President would be in post for 3 years; a President elect being elected who would also serve for 3 years and then become President. The title of Vice President was changed to Ex-President.

- The Special Representatives: Editor of the Journal, Benevolent and Scholarship Fund Secretaries, and Swimming and Music Representatives would become Council members whilst in Office with a right to vote.

- Honorary membership would now be granted to those who had given something 'special' to the League.

With the help of some loyal members who served on Council several times, it continued to manage League affairs effectively until its closure in 2010. In 2007 the Constitution was changed to allow Council members and Officers to be in post over their prescribed periods to ensure continuity of management for the last few years.

The Final League Council

GUY'S HOSPITAL NURSES' LEAGUE COUNCIL 2010

President: Miss P. M. Jefferies

Chairman: Miss A. M. E. Russell   **Vice-Chairman:** Miss A. Howard

Hon. Treasurer: Mrs E. D. Stebbing   **Hon. Assistant Treasurer:** Mrs J. M. Freeman

Hon. Secretary: Mrs L. E. Byers   **Hon. Assistant Secretary:** Miss G. M. Moore

Members of the Council:

Honorary Officers (ex officio)
Representative of the Guy's and St. Thomas Trust: Ms Eileen Sills
Chief Executive of the Guy's and St. Thomas' Charity: Mr P. Hewitt

Representatives of Honorary Members:
Mrs R. Shackle   Ms S. Carnall

Representatives of Past and Present Nurses:

Mrs M. Gray	Mrs M. Preston
Mrs P. Bosdet	Miss A. Burnapp
Mrs E. Morley	Mrs I. Stevens
Miss B. Faulkner	Mrs M. Gillies
Mrs S. Hudson	Mrs J. Johnston
Ms C. Manson	Miss A. Packer
Hon. Mrs M. Penney	

Privileged Members:
Mrs C. M. Hubble
Miss M. Fabling
Miss B. Faulkner

Special Representatives:

Editor of the Journal:	Miss A. Howard
Secretary to the Benevolent Fund:	Miss M. Jones-Evans
Secretary to the Scholarship Fund:	Mrs J. Short
Music Representative:	Mrs J. Pye
Archive Representative:	Miss B. Faulkner

Vice-Presidents:

Mrs E. M. Collings	Mrs M. J. Davis OBE
Mrs B. M. Herbert	Mrs J. Pye
Miss B. N. Stevenson	

A League meeting in 2000

The last League Council meeting 22nd September 2010

The Officers of the League 2010

PRESIDENT
Pam Jefferies

CHAIRMAN
Alison Russell

HONORARY TREASURER
Doreen Stebbing

HONORARY SECRETARY
Laura Byers

VICE CHAIRMAN
Andie Howard

ASST HON. SECRETARY
Gill Moore

SCHOLARSHIP FUND
SECRETARY
Juliet Short

ASST HON TREASURER
Julia Freeman

BENEVOLENT FUND
SECRETARY
Margaret Jones-Evans

The League Office

Although the business of the League was managed by the Council, a huge amount of hard work has taken place outside Council meetings to keep the League running.

Over the years, a number of loyal helpers, mostly volunteers, have devoted much of their time and efforts behind the scenes, running the League Office and assisting with the administration.

The collection of subscriptions and keeping the register up to date was a huge task, particularly before the computer age, with every envelope addressed by hand.

The first of the assistants was May Smith, who, although not a volunteer, as the Clerk and Secretary in Matron's Office her workload greatly increased at the founding of the League. One of her tasks was the writing of the minutes of Council and the AGM which she did for over thirty years in precise longhand script.

This is an extract from 1924:

Miss Zygouras replaced Miss Smith as secretary and assisted with League administration for more than 30 years from 1933. In 1960 at the AGM it was reported that she had had to have her glasses changed as a result of correcting and re-correcting hundreds of names and addresses for the register!

Honorary members were also of great help in dealing with the workload. When Miss Zygouras retired, the Matron felt that due to increased workload, her new secretary could not manage League work. Mrs Blackburn, wife of one of the Consultant Surgeons, agreed to assist in the Office and was appointed as League Assistant Honorary Secretary a post she held for fourteen years.

From 1984, the Honorary Secretary's post was no longer held by the Matron, and this post holder then took a much more hands on role in League administration.

The first of these was Barbara Stevenson (Stevie) who ran the office for the next eleven years, ably assisted by the Assistant Hon. Secretary, Muriel Theisen (Thei), Faith Rigby, who was Treasurer, member Edna Collings, and Honorary member Rachel Townsin who had previously helped in the Office from 1966–81.

The last Honorary Secretary to run the League Office was Laura Byers, (2002–10) who with Treasurer Doreen Stebbing (2001–10) has come in for a day every week to manage the League through to its closure. They were assisted by Gill Moore (Honorary Secretary 1998–2010) who was also working full time as a Trust ward sister.

CHAPTER FIVE

Financial Matters

The League has always managed its financial affairs well, balancing income with expenditure in most years. In the beginning its main income was from member subscriptions and the main expenditure was in paying off the loan for the Cottage and the printing of the Nurses Guide and Register, the latter being somewhat defrayed by including adverts. In most years this resulted in a small positive balance on League accounts and occasional income also came from performances by the music club or dramatic society.

From the start the League was determined to pay off its debt for the Cottage in Honor Oak Park and by 1916 the original debt on the cottage of nearly £4,000 had been reduced to £1,000.

Later on in the life of the League, as members left legacies in their wills, funds increased, particularly for benevolent purposes and financial management became more complicated.

The League has also invested wisely over the years. By 1930 it had bought £1,100 of War Loan Bonds and the dividend from the investments covered nearly three quarters of the cost of the Nursing Guide & Register.

The Honorary Treasurer of the League has always been appointed from the League Council and was frequently an honorary member. The first was Mrs Lauriston Shaw who handed over to Mrs Bryant in 1904.

The Treasurer did not seem to require any experience of financial management, however, the Clerk to the Governors was always ready to help, advise and the Hospital accountant would audit the accounts.

The first Treasurers were also tasked with raising funds and support for the League from the Patrons, Governors, Consultants etc. Each year the Treasurer would present the Accounts at the AGM.

GUY'S HOSPITAL PAST AND PRESENT NURSES' LEAGUE.
Income and Expenditure Account for the year ended February 28th, 1918.

INCOME.	£	s.	d.	EXPENDITURE.	£	s.	d.
To Subscriptions:—				By Rent, Rates and Taxes	£62	11	8
Hon. Members £53 0 0				„ Household Requisites	12	12	6
Present Members 106 11 3				„ Upkeep of Tennis Courts	8	19	0
Past Members 45 18 6				„ Tennis and Garden Requisites ...	2	2	9
Life Members ... · 51 6 0				„ Coal	12	4	3
	256	15	9	„ Printing and Stationery	35	12	3
„ Grants:—				„ Salaries and Health Insurance ...	21	17	6
Nurses' Institution 4 17 6				„ Postage and Cheques	9	9	5
Nurses' Raphael Fund 20 0 0				„ Repairs and Furnishing	6	17	6
	24	17	6	„ Sundry Expenses	4	19	11
„ Nursing Guide and Register:—					177	6	9
Sale of Copies 11 4 0				„ Cost of League Badges	22	11	6
Advertisements 25 14 6				„ Railway Tickets (Half Fare)... ...	31	5	0
	36	18	6	„ Honorarium to Caretaker	5	0	0
„ Sale of Badges	20	11	0	„ Christmas Gift to Nurses abroad ...	5	0	0
„ Donation, Nurses' Christmas Present	0	10	0				
„ Sundry Receipts	0	1	8	Total Expenditure	241	3	3
				„ Excess of Income over Expenditure	98	11	2
	£339	14	5		£339	14	5

CAPITAL ACCOUNT.

LIABILITIES.	£	s.	d.	ASSETS.	£	s.	d.
To Outstanding Loan from the President and Governors of Guy's Hospital on the security of the Freehold Land and Premises:—				By Land at Honor Oak Park (at Cost) ... £2,520 18 5			
Amount brought forward from last year £1,000 0 0				„ Buildings erected thereon (at Cost) ... 1,388 8 6			
Less proportion repaid ... 100 0 0					3,909	6	11
„ Capital Account:—	900	0	0	„ Cash at Bankers	96	13	4
Balance brought forward from last year 3,008 3 9				„ Petty Cash in hand	0	14	8
Plus excess of Income over Expenditure for the 12 months to February 28th, 1918 ... ,... 98 11 2					97	8	0
	3,106	14	11				
	£4,006	14	11		£4,006	14	11

I have audited the above Balance Sheet and Income and Expenditure Account with the Books and Vouchers, and find them correct.
May 4th, 1918.   (Signed) W. J. CURRY, Corporate Accountant.

Accounts for 1918

For many years the Treasurers had the huge task, with the help of the secretary, of collecting the subscriptions from League members and in 1930 they also became responsible for the management of the Cosmo Bonsor Scholarship Fund and later for the Benevolent Fund account.

In 1937 the League changed its Auditors to Turquand, Youngs, McAuliffe & Co and in 1943 the Council agreed to their advice that the League set up a Reserve Fund to invest for potential future expenses such as the Nursing Guide or repairs to the Cottage.

From the 1950s onwards, although annually the excess of income over expenditure remained small, the League had healthy assets mainly due to wise investment and legacies from members.

In 1954 all the League funds, which had been in the care of the Trustees, were deposited in the National Provincial Bank.

By 1957 the assets were £13,568 in the General Fund and £2,836 in the Benevolent Fund and the Council were advised by the Clerk to the Governors to make investments in British Electricity and savings bonds. There were also funds in the Post Office Savings Bank.

By 1980 the capital in the General Fund had risen to £27,548.

In 1996, Faith Rigby, Treasurer since 1980 was asked to describe the duties of the Treasurer for the Journal:

She wrote that her 'special responsibilities' were:

a. *The annual report to the Charities Commission*
b. *The Preparation of the Corporation tax*
c. *The preparation of the books for the annual audit*

And day to day management:

a. *Collections and recording of subscriptions and donations.*
b. *Checking bank statements*
c. *Checking and paying of accounts*
d. *Management of the Benevolent Fund*[29]

Treasurers since 1964

Vivien Blaikley 1963–73

Pip Salmon 1974–79

Faith Rigby 1979–95

Marian Hubble 1996–2001

Doreen Stebbing, 2002–10 (picture on page 66)

Marian Hubble has written a short insight into the world of the League Treasurer:

It was 1996, Faith Rigby had held the post of Treasurer for 17 years and was wanting to stand down.

Betsy Morley was the League Chairman and was looking for someone to take Faith's place. At the time I was a fairly recent recruit to League Council. At my third meeting the call went out for a treasurer. Betsy stood at the exit seeking a volunteer, no-one had offered to take the post. I was the last to leave.

I was given the job!

I had no idea what this entailed beyond collecting and recording subscriptions.

Mavis Fabling was the Honorary Secretary at the time and she gently enlightened me as to what was expected of the Treasurer.

Advice was available and freely given by the Hospital Trustees, their financial advisors and our auditors.

One of my earliest tasks was to review the League's investments in order to maximise its income, particularly for the Benevolent Fund, the assets of which were at that time in excess of £400,000.

The local Nat West Bank was very obliging and I was locked away in an upstairs room whilst I sorted countless Stock and Share certificates.

Once everything was accounted for the funds were invested with COIF where they remained during my watch.

Managing the money was a shared task; my role was to ensure that the figures added up and were acceptable to the Auditors.

Being Treasurer was never a chore but five years of fun!

Benevolence

The League has a long record of benevolence towards its members and others. The first record of such generosity came in 1911 when, at the AGM, the Chairman announced that members of the League wanted to do something for others and in particular to think of those former members of staff now old and retired, who might be in need of assistance. They all knew how delightfully independent these nurses were but a proposition would be made to members as to how they could help. This was announced by Sister Lydia who said that the League now numbered over

1000 members, and in view of the fact that the members subscriptions had this year met the current expenditure, it was recommended that the sum of 10s. per week should be devoted to the maintenance of an elderly Guy's nurse in one of the King Edward Memorial Homes shortly to be established. However the Council decided it was not in a position to commit to a regular donation at this time, although they would be glad to consider other requests in the future.

During WW1 the League sent cards, small gifts and calendars to members working abroad.

In 1923 The League members raised £2,200 towards the Hospital's debt and £2,343 for Guy's Bi-centenary fund. This fund was closed in 1930 when £2,449.10s.6d had been raised and new fund commenced to raise money to equip the library and a practical class room which was being built in memory of Lord Revelstoke.

The Benevolent Fund

In 1947, Matron Dorothy Smith suggested the establishment of a separate Benevolent Fund to give financial or other assistance to any Guy's nurse in need. At that time regular grants were given at Easter and Christmas to elderly and frail nurses, some of whom also received Christmas parcels. These parcels and grants were sent every year until the late 1990s. Many elderly members now had a cupboard full of bed socks and bed jackets!

Applications to the Benevolent Fund, which were confidential were made to the Honorary Secretary and approved by the Trustees.

In 1954, following a postal vote of members, £1,000 was transferred to the Benevolent Fund from the General Fund. The fund was further boosted by generous donations from League members.

One such legacy was a house left by a Miss Hargrave in 1936. Her elderly father still lived there and the condition was that he remain there for the rest of his life. He died in 1958 when the house was sold and £2,314 was added to the Benevolent Fund.

Another generous legacy of £8,000 came in 1967 from Marion Gration who had trained at Guy's from 1902–05 and held a Sister's post there until 1942. Another member donated their stamp collection which raised £2,000.

In 1963 it was suggested that the League apply for Charitable Status for the Benevolent Fund but it was decided that the tax benefits would be small and the restrictions too great.

However a separate bank account was opened for the Fund and monies transferred from the General Account.

The Benevolent Fund was not just about money and gifts. In 1963 Matron Anne Johnson voiced her concerns at the AGM, that some elderly nurses may be alone and in need of some companionship. She appealed for members to volunteer to visit the elderly or infirm in their area. By 1964 thirty nine visitors had volunteered and a register of visitors was commenced.

In 1970, Mrs Lilian Franks, an Honorary Member of the League took up this mantle and wrote in the Journal asking for the names of members who might visit those in need and 'A Friend in Need' was created. Mrs Franks was invited to sit on Council to represent this cause.

In 1973 it was felt that the League funds were sufficient for it to apply for Charity Status, which granted it exemption from income tax.

In 1996 the League received a huge legacy of £154,000 from the estate of the late Dorothy Holland. A sub-committee of Council, including a financial advisor, was set up to manage the considerable funds.

This committee recommended that the Trustees were replaced by a committee of Officers chaired by a Benevolent Fund Secretary. Brenda Faulkner was appointed to this post and co-opted onto Council.

Flowers sent to members on their 80th and subsequent birthdays

In 1997 the funds were transferred to the Charities Official Investment Fund (COIF) who were experienced in managing larger sums of money.

Following the re-organisation of the Benevolent Fund, members in need were invited to apply for an annual grant and this was given to a number of people who required ongoing support. The visitors scheme for elderly and infirm members was also re-established by Brenda Faulkner and Jill Johnstone.

In 2004 it was decided to send a calendar with historical Guy's pictures to all members who had qualified 60 years previously, and this continued every Christmas until 2009.

Flowers were also sent to members on their 80th and subsequent birthdays.

Benevolent Fund Secretaries

Brenda Faulkner
1998 & 2000–2006

Jill Johnstone
1999

Margaret Evans-Jones
2007–2010

The Scholarship Fund

The Scholarship Fund was created in 1929 in memory of Sir Cosmo Bonsor, who had been a great supporter of the League since its founding and was its first Chairman. Fund raising commenced immediately with £76 being raised from a concert put on by the Choral Society and a Greek play performed by the Dramatic Society.

Sister Florence Taylor, then Assistant Sister Tutor, was an enthusiastic fund raiser, organising sales of work, sideshows at fetes and sweepstakes.

By 1936 the fund had reached over £1,000 and the first scholarship of £30 was awarded to Miss Gladys Kathleen Bush, who intended to take a course of study in psychological nursing.

In 1940 the scholarship was offered for the first time for a specific purpose, namely the Sister Tutor's course at the College of Nursing. Unfortunately no-one applied.

On the death of Lady Mabel Bonsor in 1944 the fund was renamed the Sir Cosmo and Lady Mabel Bonsor Scholarship Fund. The award remained at £30–£50 per annum until the early 1960s when it was raised to £60. On advice of the Finance Department, in 1964 the Fund's assets, which then comprised £1,750, were invested to bring in an annual income which would be used for the Scholarship award. This meant that the award could be increased to £200 per annum.

The original concept of the fund was for a travelling scholarship to enable League members to study a special branch of nursing abroad. Since 1899 nurses had been attending the Congress of the International

A group from Guy's in the Congress Hall of the Bonadventure Hotel, Montreal, in June 1969. Back row L-R, M. Wilcock (1932), M. Rowland (1957), G. A. Dickson (1964), M. Benson (1936), P. Ashworth (1952), V. Beuret (1964), M. Duncombe (1943), J. Page (1949), M. Walker (1950), A. J. Williams (1941). Front row L.-R., O. Branch (1942), B. M. Robertson (1938), M. Day (1951), T. Swindells (1949), P. Southwell (1956)

Council of Nurses all over the world and in 1946 it was suggested that scholarship funding be awarded to assist with the expenses of attending the Congress in the USA. In 1961, the League gave £1,000, including money from the General Fund for three members to attend the Congress in Australia. Matron also attended, generously funded by the Board of Governors.

From the early days the Scholarship Fund was advertised in the National nursing press, and later in the Guy's Gazette and the annual Journal. At first it was only available to members currently working at the hospital but in 1939, to encourage more applicants, it was opened to all League members.

In 1999 the Scholarship was reviewed in the light of the current needs of post graduate nurse education. The Sir Cosmo and Lady Mabel Bonsor award would now be a triennial award with the aim of it funding a degree course. The Charity Commission agreed that some Benevolent Fund money could be used for scholarship and an annual Dorothy Holland award was set up comprising 25% of the interest of the Benevolent Fund.

A Scholarship Fund Secretary was appointed to sit on Council. The first being Andrew MacCallum, the Deputy Director of Nursing at the Guy's & St Thomas Hospital Trust.

The Scholarship Fund will continue after the League closes and together with the Benevolent Fund is being managed by the Guy's & St Thomas' Foundation Trust Charity. It will be available to all nurses who have worked for Guy's & St Thomas' for a minimum of one year as well as League members.

Scholarship Fund Secretaries

Andrew MacCallum	*Prue Bosdet*	*Juliet Short*
1999–2000	*2001–2006*	*2007–2010*

CHAPTER SIX

The Life of the League:
The First 50 Years

T he League has lived a long and busy life during a century of major change and progress, with huge advancements in medicine and technology. Its members have seen major developments in nursing, nurse education and the role of the nurse. Members have served through two world wars, experienced State Registration and the formation of regulatory bodies for nurses, and witnessed increased specialisation in nursing and advanced nursing practice. Amongst other things, they have experienced the founding of the NHS, the demise of the Matron and the introduction of nurse prescribing.

Apart from the achievements of the clubs and societies, League events and the successes of its members have been many and varied over the years, here are some of the more significant.

1900 onwards

Working Abroad: The British Empire was still going strong in the earlier days of the League and it was common practice for nurses to go and work in the 'colonies'. Many overseas hospitals were staffed by British nurses and a number of Guy's League members were appointed as Matrons.

Most joined Queen Alexandra's Nursing Service or Lady Minto's Indian Nursing Association and served in countries such as India, East Africa, Palestine, Egypt, Mesopotamia, Ceylon (Sri Lanka) and Salonika.

Several members went to nurse the wounded from the Boer War between 1899–1902 and some received honours for their service. Miss R. B. Brereton received the Royal Red Cross; Miss A. Davidson (Sister Job) and Miss I. Burdett were given an enamelled badge for nursing at the front and Nurse Mary Joy received the Order of St John of Jerusalem. Many Guy's nurses continued to work abroad until well into the 1970s.

1902

The Nursing Guide: The first major achievement of the League was the publishing of the first edition of the Nursing Guide which included a register of nurses who had trained or were training at Guy's. This was another of Sarah Swift's ideas and it was the first such register to be printed in the UK. There were fourteen editions in all, the last being in 1960; more of these in Chapter 10.

1903

Post graduate education: In 1903 Sarah Swift introduced another innovative idea, namely, a post graduate course of six lectures. As usual, Sarah Swift was well ahead of the field as this was the first such scheme to be started in England. She asked for a vote of approval from past members at the AGM and the suggestion was greeted enthusiastically. The lectures commenced later that year and were also typed out and sent to members who could not attend them. The early lectures were given by the medical staff though later also given by nurses. The course cost League members 5s and later non members were also allowed to attend for 7s. 6d.

Examples of the types of lectures given:

In 1910 Dr H. C. Cameron gave a series of lectures including one entitled 'Recent changes in treatment in the Medical wards'. He described the new method of treating oedema by a salt free diet and the great benefits of the application of heat to the joints for chronic joint diseases, such as osteo and rheumatoid arthritis.

In the same series in 1910; Mr E. C. Hughes spoke about recent changes in surgery. He compared the treatment of appendicitis and peritonitis with that of five to ten years previously. The peritoneal cavity was no longer washed out which had resulted in a major reduction in shock and an improvement in the mortality rate which could be as low as 15% whereas ten years before it had been as high as 90–95%!

1908

The League Badge: In 1908 the League adopted their own badge. Made in bronze, the badge carried the hospital shield in the centre in black and white enamel and the hospital motto: 'Dare Quam Accipere' – 'It is better to give receive' was engraved across the bottom.

The badge cost 3s. 1d. and could only be worn by the League President or members who had a certificate of training at Guy's. If a member left the League the badge had to be returned and if they lost the badge they were fined 10s. 6d.

All members had to sign a declaration that they would adhere to the above rules.

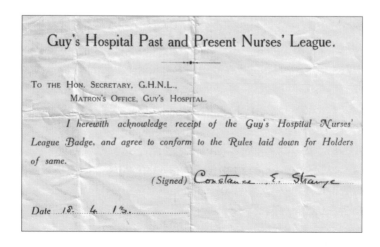

Guy's Hospital Past and Present Nurses' League.

To the Hon. Secretary, G.H.N.L.,
    Matron's Office, Guy's Hospital.

I herewith acknowledge receipt of the Guy's Hospital Nurses' League Badge, and agree to conform to the Rules laid down for Holders of same.

(Signed) Constance E. Strange

Date 15. 4. 13.

In 1911, Matron declared that Staff Nurses, when working on the wards should wear their Guy's badges as a mark of distinction between them and Head nurses.

The badge could be replaced at the discretion of the Council, though members had to account for its loss. The reasons were wide-ranging: Miss Nash's badge was lost whilst undergoing repairs at a local jeweller, Staff Nurse Sharp, Miss Groves and Mrs Hill had inadvertently sent theirs to the laundry (this was a favourite excuse) and Miss Seaman had lost hers in a garden in Labrador while serving with the Grenfell Mission. The Council were disturbed to hear that Staff Nurse Mann's badge had been stolen from her uniform while she was working in the Operating Theatres, while Mrs Innes had lost hers while taking home a member of staff who was unwell and Miss Fewster's badge had gone missing in snow in Newfoundland.

Mrs Bruck's explanation was the most dramatic – hers had been lost during the war when her home had been destroyed by enemy action.

1909

Sarah Swift retired: The League founder and first Honorary Secretary retired and Miss Louisa Haughton was appointed as Matron.

New Council members: Nine associate members were voted onto Council. These came from the Patrons and Patronesses who supported the League from its inception by making a donation. By 1916 these were described as Honorary members who were invited to join the League and were mostly ladies who were associated with Guy's in some way, the wives of Consultants or Hospital Governors.

1910

Mr Cosmo Bonsor, was elected President of the Hospital and had to resign as League Chairman.

Viscount Goschen was appointed as Treasurer of Guy's and became Chairman of the League. Later he was to be President of Guy's until his retirement in 1944.

George Joachim
2nd Viscount Goschen

1911

The first Vice Presidents were elected to the League: They were Viscountess Goschen, wife of the Hospital Treasurer, Miss (later Dame) Sarah Swift and Mr (later Sir) Cosmo Bonsor. The title of Vice President was thereafter given to those who had made a special contribution to the League.

1914

The First World War: This was the first major conflict since the start of the League and had a profound impact on League members as it did on the whole country.

At the outbreak of war League members immediately responded. Each League was asked to form a unit of nurses for a Nursing Corps to care for wounded soldiers. Miss Gladys White, Sister Surgery, and four others were some of the first to form such a unit in November 1914. Other members went to France in December 1914.

On 18th December nine nurses, including Miss A. M. Rogers, from Guy's left for Bordeaux. At this time it was reported that there were less wounded men than expected so no more nurses were required. As history records this situation would tragically change very soon.

The first group of nurses leave Guy's for war: with them is Matron Louisa Haughton

By February 1915 The Brigade Hospital of the Order of St John had been set up in France with two Guy's trained nurses as Matron and Assistant Matron.

In the same month Sister V. M. Kiddle of Guy's was the first to be mentioned in despatches.

Sarah Swift, who had retired, was recalled to be Matron-in-Chief of the Joint War Committee of the St John Ambulance Association and the British Red Cross Society (BRCS). During the war her department was responsible for more than 6,000 trained nurses, overseeing their selection and dispatch to hospitals at home and abroad, and also for interviewing the Voluntary Aid Workers.

The War Office approached the Governors to provide a ward for wounded officers. Stephen Ward, a 50 bedded medical ward was cubicled and renamed The Officers' section. Grace Shield, 'Sister Stephen', nicknamed 'Sister Susie' by the Officers after the patter song 'Sister Susie's sewing shirts for soldiers', was put in charge of it. It was recorded that under her care, of more than a thousand officers who were admitted for treatment to her ward, only 12 died.

More than 500 Guy's nurses and League members were involved in the war and many of them received awards for service and bravery.

Emily MacManus, Guy's trained nurse, League member and later Guy's Matron, who worked in France, including a stint near the front line, describes some of the dangers faced for serving nurses in her book; 'Matron of Guy's':

> 'On a quick journey along the wooden platform towards my tent, suddenly the sky appeared to split; a great piece of metal, with a bolt and a round knob on it, fell at my feet'.

On another occasion treating soldiers who had been gassed:

> 'Soon I found that I too was getting gassed. The fumes from the khaki clothing, removed, but lying under each man on his stretcher, was poisoning me. Laboriously I emptied each man's pockets and flung out armloads of reeking khaki. When I had finished, my own forearms and neck were burnt red and sore from the mustard, my eyes and nose were pouring with fluid, and I had lost my voice'.[30]

Five Guy's nurses lost their lives serving their country: Evelyn Hopkins, Constance Dean, Elsie Gladstone, Agnes Woodhead and Mary Morrell

IN MEMORY OF

EVELYN HOPKINS.   NOV
CONSTANCE DEAN.   DEC
ETHEL M. GLADSTONE.   JAN
AGNES S. WOODHEAD.   MAY
MARY L. MORRELL.
WHO DIED IN THE SERVICE OF T

Their Name Liveth for

The Memorial Plaque in the Chapel

are all remembered on a brass plaque in the Guy's Chapel. Many of them survived the conflict but still serving, succumbed to the influenza pandemic that followed the end of the war.

Elsie Gladstone had trained at Guy's between 1912 and 1914.

Newly qualified, she joined Q. A. I. M. N. S. She served on a Hospital Ship and at a Casualty Clearing Station. She was awarded the Royal Red Cross Medal but she died of flu before she could receive it. She was buried in Belgium with military honours.

Elsie Gladstone's grave is at the Belgrade Communal Cemetery, Namur, Belgium. She is one of only two female military casualties of WW1 buried in Belgium.

Elsie Gladstone's grave in Belgium

1915

League member appointed as Nursing Mirror Editor: Miss Emily Margaret Fox, for many years Matron of the Prince of Wales Hospital, Tottenham, was made editor of the Nursing Mirror. She was the first nurse to take this post. The British Journal of Nursing reported her appointment:

'Miss Fox was trained at Guy's Hospital which, unlike several large London hospitals, permits freedom of conscience and action to its nursing staff on professional affairs. In accepting the editorship of the journal in question, Miss Fox, who is a professional woman, accepts responsibility that justice shall be done to her professional colleagues, and we wish her the moral courage to demand it'.[31]

1916

College of Nursing: (later Royal College of Nursing) was founded by Sarah Swift with support from Dr Arthur Stanley, Sir Cooper Perry and several Matrons from London Teaching Hospitals. The initial aims of the College were to organise the Nursing Profession, to secure State Registration for the trained nurse, to maintain a register of trained nurses, to protect the interests of trained nurses, to raise and maintain the standard of training, to establish a uniform, curriculum of training and final examinations and to in every way promote the advancement of professional nurses.

At the 1917 AGM, Sarah Swift invited the League members to join the College of Nursing and in 1918 this was followed up by a letter sent to all League members.

Again there was opposition from the BJN.

'With the letter are included an Application Form, and Reasons for joining the College, but not a copy of the Constitution. The gist of the letter is practically a demand upon the part of Guy's officials nominated on to the College Council, that an electorate should be provided amongst the nurses of the League. It is written:– On the Council of the College, Guy's ought to be well represented amongst other hospitals, and the votes of Guy's nurses are needed to place their representatives there. It is well known that the extremely autocratic Constitution of the College, which practically supports all professional liberty of the nursing profession as a whole, emanated from the reactionary policy of Sir Cooper Perry, the Medical Superintendent, and Miss Sarah Swift, the Matron of Guy's Hospital in 1905, when this Constitution was submitted to the Board of Trade, as suitable for a governing body for free British women'.[32]

Again the opposition was not justified and Sarah Swift's measured and pragmatic approach proved to be successful.

In 1928, the RCN received its Royal Charter, and today it has over 395,000 members, its Patron is Queen Elizabeth II and it is the main union representation for most professional UK nurses.

In 1919 the College asked an MP to put forward a private member's bill to introduce regulation for nurses. This resulted in the Registration of Nurses Act and the formation of the General Nursing Council.

1924

Franchise for nursing: Although women over 30 had achieved the vote in 1918, nurses living in hospital accommodation were not included.

An objection to nurses being put on the register had been lodged by the Unionist Agent on the grounds that their place of residence disentitled them to franchise.

This matter was brought to the attention of the Southwark Registration Officer and Town Clerk, Mr P. Gray.

The statute relating to franchise stated that anyone who inhabited a dwelling house by virtue of any office, service or employment was deemed to be an inhabitant occupier of that dwelling and therefore entitled to vote.

In a test case involving League member Mary Baker-Jones, a probationer at Guy's, Mr Draper ruled that a contract of service had been entered into between herself and the Board of Governors and this could be interpreted as forming a relationship of 'master and servant'.

He also decided that as she occupied a bedroom in the Nurses Home, this could be interpreted as living in a 'dwelling house' and therefore entitled her to Local Government and Parliamentary franchise.

He added that this decision would apply to all other probationer nurses and others whose circumstances were the same.

1925

January: Bi-centenary of the opening of Guy's in 1725: A celebration in Southwark Cathedral was attended by six past Matrons, including League members, Victoria Jones, Esther Young, Florence Nott-Bower and Dame Sarah Swift. They made a notable picture as they walked in procession to the Cathedral.

October: Dame Sarah Swift: was elected as President of the College of Nursing.

1929

Guy's Hospital Ladies Association: League member Miss Venning, formerly Sister Lydia, founded the Nurses League Branch of this association. By the end of the first year there were 56 members and this had increased to 150 by 1934. The Ladies Association founded in 1895 to provide clothing for destitute patients, later also provided other extra comforts and amenities. It was to eventually merge with the Guild of Ex-Patients to form the Friends of Guy's in 1972.

Death of Sir Cosmo Bonsor: League members were very sad to learn of the death of Sir Cosmo Bonsor, first League Chairman and Vice President, who had been a true friend of the League and supporter of the nurses for over 30 years.

The members decided to start a Scholarship Fund as a memorial to him, which would provide a special course of post graduate study for a League member.

League beds: Two beds were endowed in the Hospital for the use of League members who required hospital treatment.

1934

William James Curry: a former Clerk to the Governors of Guy's admitted at The Old Bailey that he had appropriated about £3,000 from Guy's including war loans of £1,100 belonging to the Nurses' League. He was sentenced to 3 years imprisonment. Unfortunately there was no hope of recovery of this money and the League had to approach the Governors to help them through this difficult time.

July: Lilian Lang: League member was congratulated by the Deputy Coroner for South London on her bravery in stopping two runaway horses pulling a van in the Borough High Street. Seeing the van driver lying before the front wheels of the van she seized the reins to stop the horses, being dragged for some way, lifted off her feet and tearing her clothes. Sadly the driver did not survive. When commended for her bravery she modestly said that it was simply the result of her training and that any trained nurse would have done the same.

1938: War predicted: At the AGM, the members were reminded that they may be called on to serve their country in case of war. Emily MacManus began compiling a Roll of Past Nurses who would be willing to help in that event.

1939

The Second World War: League members made a major contribution during the second world war, nursing at Guy's or one of the three hospitals in Kent where most of the patients were transferred or in posts at other hospitals in London and throughout the country. Many also joined the army, navy or air force nursing services. The student nurses all went to the hospitals in Kent but a small number of trained nurses stayed at Guy's with Deputy Matron Florence Wittrick. Guy's was bombed many times during the war sustaining significant damage but the nurses remained on duty providing emergency care for the casualties. Fortunately no nurses were killed or injured at Guy's but several serving in the forces or working abroad lost their lives. Eileen Ievers and Joan Pitt, missing at sea, presumed killed. Marjorie Livingstone, missing after the fall of Singapore and presumed dead, and Norah Holroyd a member of the Civil Nursing Reserve.

League member Sheila Greaves, later Mrs Fox won the George Medal for her bravery on Anzio Beach.

Nurses serving overseas wrote to Emily MacManus of their experiences which she reported at the AGM:

Margaret Thorpe was following the eighth army through the Middle East:

Just before Christmas, 1942, she and seven other Sisters were very busy in a Casualty Clearing Station at Tobruk. They were there for three weeks with bitterly cold weather, and many days of rain which nearly washed their tents away. Later Miss Thorpe advanced to Tripoli and Medimine where she was busy admitting patients who had only been wounded a matter of hours, still with their field dressings untouched. On one night they admitted up to five hundred, and there were stretchers everywhere even in the Sergeants Mess.[33]

Years later in the League Journals, members remembered their war experiences:

Monica Dow: 1941, while billeted with a family in Farnborough, Kent:

Big Ben struck 9pm. The news started, the radio dimmed and we heard no more – not an unusual occurrence when the enemy was about. The siren wailed its whining war song and the gun firing was terribly heavy. Bombs came whistling down, one after the other, near and far.

There were seven of us ready to meet our end at any moment. The gunfire and the buzzing of the planes was terrific. More and more bombs fell; there were strange noises in the sky as well as the perpetual rumble of enemy planes. I had walked home in my cotton uniform dress and we had had to rush out of the house into the shelter before I could get changed. The shelter door had blown off and none of us could sleep. I got colder and colder. The all clear went at 5am but I had to get up at 6am to go to work. At the Hospital there was no gas and we were very understaffed. Everything had to be boiled on three coke stoves – it was very very difficult.[34]

Margaret Jeans: 1943: nursing at Guy's

I can remember the night of the big fire-bomb raid. Every member of staff was out to help douse the incendiary bombs. All the patients were evacuated by Greenline bus to the base hospitals. The last patient having left, the nurses were given their instructions:

> 'You will walk to the large shelter in Blackfriars – there you will be given a hot drink, get some rest and be back here at 8am for duty'

It is a good walk from Guy's to Blackfriars but we thought nothing of it. I particularly remember that night – it was strangely awesome and magically beautiful. The constant explosions swept over us like the music of terror, fires surrounded us and buildings crashed. ARP, firemen and any one else nearby lent a hand to rescue and comfort the wounded and the panic stricken.

We walked on our way unscathed by the horror. The bedlam could have been an eerie orchestra's playing of Handel's firework music.

In contrast, next morning, our return was through war weary streets where some buildings remained whole while others smouldered. There was a strange smell around us and the weird red glow of smouldering fires. Yet the city was coming to life, with the cheerful greetings of the milkman on his round and the ARP wardens and Policemen busy clearing the mess. A dazed population emerged from their shelters to resume their daily round and common task.[35]

1946: November: Nurse appointed as League Chairman: Following the resignation of Lady Cunliffe and in the aftermath of WW2, as the League regrouped, Kitty Bulleid, agreed to act as temporary Chairman for a period of four years and this was to stretch to eleven. She was the first Chairman who was a nurse and it meant that at last the Nurses' League was being run solely by nurses.

1947

January: Emily MacManus was awarded the C.B.E: for her services to the country as Sector Matron during the war.

June: Nurses' Prize Giving: For the first time this was held as a separate event; previously it had always been part of the League AGM.

CHAPTER SEVEN

The Life of the League: 1950–2000

At the beginning of the second fifty years of the League, members were adjusting to two major events; the after effects of the second world war and the major impact on health services following the introduction of the NHS in 1948.

1950

Nurses' Representative Council: In November 1925 a Nurses Representative Council had been created at Guy's and in 1949 they asked if they might have representation on Council. This was approved and the secretary of this group was invited to sit on the League Council.

New Nursing Guide published: This was the thirteenth edition and penultimate edition of the Nursing Guide and the first since 1937.

1957

The National Council of Nurses: In 1957 The League began discussions about the possible affiliation with the National Council of Nurses. This organisation had been founded in the early 1900s and it is not clear why the Guy's League had waited until this time to consider this option. However the National Council of Nurses had been founded by Mrs Bedford Fenwick who was also its President until her death in 1947. Mrs Fenwick had been critical of the Guy's League in the past which may have explained their reluctance to join.

A sub committee of the League Council unanimously agreed that the League should be affiliated with the National Council of Nurses.

It seemed that of all the twelve London teaching hospitals only Guy's and St George's were not affiliated. The total annual subscription would be £402 and Guy's would be entitled to seven delegates.

There were disadvantages: in order to afford the subscription, membership fees would have to be doubled and the League would have to comprise only trained nurses currently on the General Nursing Council's register, so the student nurses, Honorary members and older members no longer working would be excluded. The League Constitution would also need to be amended to reflect the new rules.

League members were all asked to vote for the proposal to join this organisation and by May, 761 responses had been received. In favour were 367 and against 463, so the majority of members were clear that the disadvantages of joining outweighed any benefits for the League and its current membership.

Election of League President & Chairman: New procedures to elect the League President & Chairman were proposed by the Honorary Secretary and approved by Council. The President would be nominated and elected by League members and the Chairman nominated from Council members and elected by Council.

Florence Taylor was elected as Chairman and Emily MacManus as President.

1958

The Evelina Children's Hospital nurses were invited to join the League. The Evelina Children's Hospital had been associated with Guy's since 1947.

The Evelina nurses accepted this offer and were asked to nominate a member to sit on Council. Their first representative was Margaret Duncombe.

October: The first League cocktail party took place. The catering manager felt he could not provide a good party for less than 10s a head. The League subsidised this by 2s. 6d for each member. It was described as an outstanding success. In appreciation the League gave a 2 guinea theatre voucher to the catering officer, a guinea gift token to the Dining Room Superintendent and 100 cigarettes each to the chefs!

1960

February: League 'guest' members: Council agreed that Mrs Brunt Green who had worked at Guy's but not trained there, and had joined as an Associate member could be allowed to remain as a member after leaving Guy's.

October: League donation to New Guy's House: The League donated a Bronze Plaque of the Head of Thomas Guy to commemorate the opening of New Guy's House, the new surgical block. This is no longer on view as it has been covered over during the provision of a Patient Transport waiting area.

November: Fourteenth and last Nurses' handbook issued. It was decided to give a copy to all student nurses on completion of their training.

1962

League Constitution revised: Non Guy's trained nurses could now be invited to join the League as Associate members. After completing three years service at Guy's they would be eligible to become full members.

This was a timely decision as a new Matron was appointed in 1962 on the retirement of Jean Recknell. She was Anne Johnson, the first Matron of Guy's who had not trained there, and as Matron she became *ex-officio* Honorary Secretary of the League.

Hilda Gration memorial: The League commenced a fund in memory of the much loved long serving Principal Tutor. Hilda Gration was the first to hold the new post of 'Sister Tutor' in 1924. By the end of 1963 the fund had reached over £800. It was agreed that it should be used to furnish a Reference Library in the School of Nursing to be called the Hilda Gration Room.

1964

League membership reaches 3,000

July: A Council Sub-Committee was formed to discuss a new format for the League magazine.

August: First male League member: Mr Trevor Clay, then Deputy Assistant Matron in the York Clinic and later to be General Secretary of the RCN, became the first male member to join the League.

Trevor Clay

1965: The League donated a carved Guy's crest in memory of Lord Cunliffe. The Crest was made locally by the Lettering Centre, an old established firm in the Borough, on the site of the old Marshalsea Prison. The crest hangs in the Burfoot Court Room, at Guy's.

1966

Spring – The new Journal was launched: (see Chapter 10)
AGM: 'Past and Present' dropped
A proposal was made to discontinue 'Past and Present' in the title of the League and change it to 'Guy's Hospital Nurses' League'. This was seconded by Miss Titley and agreed by those present.

1967

April: League Badge discontinued: Traditionally the League badge could only be awarded to Guy's trained nurses who had gained their Hospital Certificate.

The fourth compulsory year of training was discontinued so students could be awarded their badge on qualifying after three years. In 1962, non Guy's trained nurses could join the League but were not eligible for a badge and to avoid any distinction between members, the Council requested the Governors to award a Hospital Badge and the League badge was discontinued. The Hospital badge was the same as the old League Badge apart from GHNL being replaced by Guy's Hospital.

1969

Resignation of Matron and League Honorary Secretary: Miss Anne Johnson resigned at short notice. Miss Linda Titley, previously a Deputy Matron, and currently Matron of St Charles Hospital, Ladbroke Grove, agreed to delay her retirement and take the post *pro tem*.

1971

State Enrolled Nurses invited to be League members: A sub-committee of Council proposed that all nursing staff within the Guy's Group should become eligible to be Associate or Full League members. Associates would be student nurses after their Introductory Period and non Guy's trained nurses who had worked there for a minimum of six months. The latter could be full members after three years at Guy's.

The Salmon Report was introduced. This re-organised the senior nursing structure and discontinued the title 'Matron' and Miss White therefore became the Principal Nursing Officer, General Nursing Division. Despite the new title she remained as Honorary Secretary of the League.

The Old Matron's House renamed: Emily MacManus House. As there was no longer a Matron living on site it was used as an hospitality suite.

1974

Further management changes: The District Management Team was introduced and the Matron became Divisional Nursing Officer. Betty Herbert, who was appointed into this post was to reflect some years later that this re-organisation meant that the League was no longer centred in nursing administration and thus became sidelined from the focus of nursing activity in the hospital, a position from which it never recovered.

1976

250th Anniversary Celebration: The League took part in this three day event to celebrate the 250th Anniversary of the opening of Guy's. This coincided with the opening of Guy's Tower by Her Majesty the Queen. The League members attended a service in Southwark Cathedral, followed by the AGM in the newly opened Greenwood Theatre and a huge cocktail party in the evening.

1980

Emily MacManus memorial. A flowering cherry tree was planted outside Henriette Raphael in memory of Emily MacManus, who had died in 1979. Sadly the tree died after being moved in 1982 and was replaced by an inscribed wooden bench.

This is still in place today and can be found at Guy's along the path between Henriette Raphael and the Hodgkin Building (Medical School).

1981

'Matron' no longer League Honorary Secretary: This tradition that had dated from the founding of the League in 1900 ended when the current Matron, now re-named The Divisional Nursing Officer, felt unable to take on the role. Despite her retirement Betty Herbert agreed to continue in post.

Emily MacManus memorial bench

1982

A New Health Authority formed: Guy's was now part of the Lewisham and North Southwark Health Authority. There was much concern in the Hospital and the League that the name of Guy's did not appear in the title. The League Council were worried about the effect on recruitment to the League.

1983

Constitution changed: Associate membership of the League was now not compulsory for student nurses, for the first time since 1902. They were now invited to join the League after their three month's introductory period.

1985

Consultative Document: The League was asked by the District Administrator of the new Health Authority, to give views on a Consultative document on local health services. At this time the League was still valued as representing current nursing views.

January: The League were informed of new uniform regulations:

- Registered nurses were to wear a blue and white striped dress
- Strings to be abolished
- Learners (student nurses) would wear paper caps
- The Guy's cap would continue to be worn by Staff Nurses
- Outdoor uniform was to be abolished.[36]

There is no record of League member's comments on these changes.

New League members sought: Members of Council spoke to newly qualified nurses at their evaluation day to canvas new members. It was agreed to restart the practice of sending congratulations to newly qualified Guy's nurses with an application form to join the League. This became a regular recruitment strategy.

First Male Honorary male member of Council: Mr L. Salmon was the first male Honorary member of Council; he was a retired Guy's ENT Consultant and the husband of League member and Treasurer, Pip Salmon.

Mr Leslie Salmon

End of an era – Guy's School of Nursing renamed.

The League were informed that the last in-take of Guy's School of nurses for training would be in May 1985. After this training would be at the Thomas Guy & Lewisham School of Nursing.

1986

League membership and name: Current membership was 2,600. Due to the new School of Nursing, members were asked to vote if the League should be re-named. Suggestions were:

- Guy's Hospital Nurses' League (current name)
- The Guy's Past and Present Nurses' League
- The Thomas Guy Past and Present Nurses' League
- The Thomas Guy and Lewisham Nurses' League.

The result of the Ballot was announced in July 1987: 332 votes received; 195 votes to keep the current name.

The Honorary Secretary wrote that she was confident that the League would flourish well into the 21st century.

> 'It is up to the present members of the League to weather any storms these changes may bring and to ensure that our organisation will continue to care for and to help the past, present and future generations of nurses trained at Guy's and Lewisham'.[37]

1987

Demise of Hospital Leagues: The Honorary Secretary spoke of the demise of other Leagues and said that if Guy's League was to survive it must face the future with confidence and look forward to celebrating the Millennium and the League's 100th birthday in the year 2000.

1990

90th Anniversary of the Founding of the League:
A limited edition Commemorative spoon was commissioned from Professor Declan Anderson to commemorate 90 years of the League. It was hand forged in silver and carried the Guy's Shield.

A commemorative plate and mug with the Guy's crest were also produced to celebrate 90 years of the League.

A Commemorative Mug and Plate were also commissioned for the 90th anniversary

Sister Janet legacy: A Silver Statuette of Thomas Guy that had belonged to Sister Janet James who had died in April had been presented to the League. This was on display at the AGM and would take pride of place at every AGM and Council meeting from now on.

1991

Dorothy Holland coffee set: Dorothy Holland, Sister Tutor at Guy's from 1925–56 (with 3 years at Addenbrookes 1939–42) who died in 1987 was given a coffee service in Mappin & Webb Princes Plate when she first left Guy's in 1939 and this had been given to the League after her death by her sister. It was sold in a Silent Auction and the money donated to the Scholarship Fund. The set was very kindly donated again to the League in 2010 and was auctioned in aid of Mercy Ships at the final AGM celebration in 2010.

Thomas Guy Statuette

The Dorothy Holland Coffee Set

Dorothy Holland League Member 1919–87
Debating Representative 1928–30
Council Member 1957–60

The Nightingale & Guy's College of Health was formed for student nurse training; causing more concerns about the future of the League.

1993

The League entered the computer age: League records were computerised. To comply with the Data Protection Act, members had to be asked if their names could appear in the register.

October: Extraordinary General Meeting re: Future of the League: This was called to discuss the future of the League as Guy's, St Thomas' and Kings Schools of Nursing had joined to form the Nightingale Institute, King's College, London University. It was anticipated that as the students were training at a University they would not feel allegiance to a particular hospital and would not want to join a Nurses' League.

A meeting had taken place between the Guy's League, officers from the Nightingale Fellowship (St Thomas' League) and King's College Hospital League and the University. Three options were proposed:

- The continuation of the Leagues as separate entities
- The amalgamation of the Leagues into one organisation
- A single Journal, possibly divided into three sections to give news of each hospital.

Discussions following these proposals felt that point 2 would be only possible a long time in the future and that point 3 would not work. At this meeting it was agreed that each League would inform their members of the issues in their next Journals and the Institute would canvass the students about a New Nurses' League.

A Guy's EGM unanimously agreed that the Guy's League should be retained and the members would be informed of this decision via the Journal.

1994

Future of Guy's: Council members were 'stunned' to learn that following the Tomlinson Report on the future of health provision in London, the St Thomas' site had been chosen as the acute Trust Hospital. A Save Guy's campaign was launched to save Guy's for patients and League members were to take a leading role in this campaign. The 1994 AGM chapel service collection was donated to the campaign.

In July 1994 Betty Herbert, then President of the League, wrote a letter to Virginia Bottomley, the Secretary of State for Health. Her emotive points were:

- *That your proposal would deprive not only the local population of the services for which Thomas Guy founded his Hospital in 1725, but also a very great number, particularly in the South East of England, of which highly specialised services since developed on a site which is uniquely accessible.*

- *That the emasculation of a world famous hospital providing facilities for its equally famous medical, dental and nursing schools would ever be justified by the considerations put together on the false premise that south east London has more beds than its population needs.*

- *That your proposals would represent the betrayal of the trust shown in Guy's by the many great and small benefactors of the Hospital and Schools over the years and particularly in recent times by Sir Philip Harris. It was recalled that you had laid the foundation stone of this uniquely important new building on the Guy's site named after him and that the Prime Minister had unveiled a plaque there also. It mystifies us that what has been described as the 'flagship' among the hospital trusts should now be earmarked for scuttling.*[38]

There is no record of a response from Virginia Bottomley.

January 1995: The 300th meeting of the League Council is celebrated with a cake.

August: Leagues first Regional Re-union takes place. Set re-unions had been happening for many years but Margaret Lamb (League President) decided to organise a regional re-union. This took place in the Cambridge area and brought together a number of members, including some elderly members who felt they could not travel to Guy's to the AGM or set re-unions. This idea was to take off over the next ten years to cover much of the South, East and West of the UK and Scotland.

1996

May: Day of Celebration: The League organised a day of celebration to commemorate the last group of nurses completing their training at Guy's.

A Royal Worcester Figurine was commissioned to mark this historic event. (see Chapter 11)

Presidents Medal: President Margaret Lamb had commissioned the President's medal, known as the 'Gong' in 1996. The medal which was a copy of Margo's own medal, was to be handed on and worn by future Presidents.

1997

March: League given the Freedom of the Borough by Southwark Council.
This took place at a Civic Award Ceremony at Dulwich College which League members attended.

The Presidents Medal

League members at the presentation ceremony

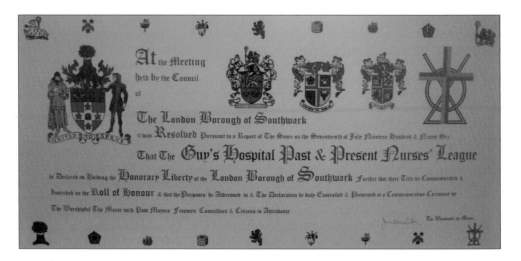

The Scroll of Honour

1997: April: Commemorative Book: Following the day of celebration in 1996, it was decided to put a history of nursing at Guy's with many old photographs which had been exhibited on the day into book form. This splendid book, with an account of 'Nursing at Guy's' 1726–1996 by Mavis Fabling and 'Nursing under Fire 1940–45' by Mrs M. K. Salmon (her personal experiences of nursing during WW2) sold 2,500 copies which were despatched from the League Office by the great efforts of Council member, The Honourable Margaret Penney.

July: Bronze Guy's Sister: The League had recently sold some items of memorabilia and it was suggested that the proceeds be put towards a bronze of a Guy's nurse which could be dedicated to all Guy's nurses past and present. Later it was agreed that this should be a half life size sculpture to be sited prominently at Guy's and an appeal was launched to fund it. It was also agreed to commission a 'miniature version' for sale to members.

October 1998 Centennial Celebrations: Discussions commenced to plan the format for 2000 AGM to celebrate the Millennium. It was to be another huge day of celebration with a service in Southwark Cathedral, lunch, an afternoon event and a review in the evening. (See Chapter 11)

CHAPTER EIGHT

The Final Ten Years: 2000–2010

The year 2000 started with world-wide Millennium celebrations and in the same year the League celebrated its centenary (see Chapter 11). The new century started with increasing uncertainty about the future of the League. From the 1980s onwards there had been increasing concern about League numbers, the recruitment of new members, particularly from younger nurses, and the relevance of the League in the changing world of nurse education.

In 1993 and 1994 the League received two significant blows: the creation of the Nightingale Institute which based nurse training at Kings College, part of London University and the decision to base all acute services at St Thomas' Hospital, greatly reducing the number of nurses working at Guy's.

2000 League celebrated its centenary: The League started the new century with a hugely successful event, held on 20th May (full account in Chapter 11).

2000 Privileged Member of Council introduced: This accolade was introduced to honour members who had given outstanding service to the League Council. It would allow the recipient to attend Council meetings and have a vote. The first Privileged member was Mavis Fabling.

2002 League membership dropped 520 in ten years: This initiated further discussion about the future of the League.

2003 Swimming Club: Due to drastically increased fees the Council decided that regretfully it could no longer support the Swimming Club.

After 103 years there was no longer a swimming representative on Council.

The future of the League: The President, Betsy Morley outlined the prospects for the League's future in the Journal.

As well as the decline in new members, all current members aged 65 or over were entitled to free membership, so annual subscriptions were also falling.

In March the Officers had discussed the option of introducing a dissolution clause to the Constitution in the event of the membership declining to an unsustainable level either financially or administratively.

Council was asked to consider the following:

- When would it be necessary to instigate a dissolution clause?
- How would the League assets be distributed?
- What legal advice and support would be required?
- What is the time frame?

It was found that a significant number of members were free, life or Honorary members as a percentage of the total number.

Possible considerations for the future were:

- Remain as we are with the implications this would have for the League
- A joint Trust League with the Nightingale Foundation at St Thomas'
- Maintain the current League for a while with a view to a joint League when necessary in the future.

The membership were asked to send their views on these options or others.

They would be discussed at the 2004 AGM.

Current Trust Nursing Staff consulted: as part of the consultation process, the Chairmen of the Guy's and St Thomas' Leagues conferred with the Trust nurses as to their interest in a Trust League. The outcomes were that the Trust staff were confused about the rationale for Leagues and were unaware of their benefits or relevance. However they were enthusiastic about a Trust League which they felt could make a positive contribution to the nursing agenda.

2004 League future: After much discussion between the three Leagues, Kings College, Guy's and the Nightingale Fellowship; the Kings College League had decided against any sort of merger. Guy's and St Thomas' were prepared to explore the potential for a merger and this would be discussed within the two Leagues. However in July 2004 it was reported to Council that The Nightingale Fellowship had voted not to join up with the Guy's League.

2004 Decision made to close the League: Having received the news from St Thomas'; the Officers had discussed how this would affect the Guy's League and after much soul searching, recommended to Council that the League should close in 2010 in a planned, dignified and organised way. Immediate discussions should take place as to the future management of the considerable funds in the Benevolent & Scholarship Funds and a sub-committee was formed to discuss this, under the Chairmanship of Vron Taylor. The proposal to close the League was put before Council in October and unanimously, though reluctantly approved.

It was decided that a rose be named to commemorate the end of the League. It was named 'Guy's Gold'.

Guy's Gold

2006 The Final AGM: The Council and Officers wanted the League to go out with a 'bang'. A Committee was formed under the Chairmanship of Betsy Morley to plan the celebrations for the final AGM in 2010.

2006 League website: The League was added to the Guy's & St Thomas' Trust website.

10th July 2010 was chosen as date for final AGM and day of celebration.

2008 The final AGM plans started to take shape: The start of the day had been an easy choice – a service in Southwark Cathedral. Guy's had always had a close association with the Cathedral and the League had celebrated two major landmarks there in recent times. The likely numbers who would want to attend a commemorative service meant the Guy's Chapel would not be an option.

Various venues had then been explored for lunch but after a vote from Council members it was decided to go for lunch at Guy's and Glaziers Hall, near London Bridge. Glaziers Hall was a beautifully restored old Livery Company building, adjacent to the Cathedral enabling easy access to the elderly or with difficult mobility. Whereas other members wanted the nostalgic option of lunch at Guy's.

For those who did not want to attend a service there would be morning coffee at Guy's and a self directed historical tour of the Guy's site.

Later cream teas, an auction of memorabilia and historical lectures by Dr Mike O'Brien were added to the plan for the day and the curator of the Gordon Museum, the world famous forensic museum, also agreed to open it for visitors.

2008 League website: A website was set up for the League at www.guyshospitalnursesleague.org.

July 2008 Trust Charity will take over the management of the League funds: The Special Purpose Fund Committee in reviewing future application for League funds will be regulated by the conditions set down in the League Constitution.

The League fund would remain separate from the Charity's other funds and would still be named The Guy's Hospital Nurses' League Fund. The Trust's Chief Nurse or her deputy would advise on scholarship fund applications.

October 2008 League membership closed: It was decided that with only two years to go new members would no longer be accepted except for those applying for access to the Benevolent or Scholarship Funds.

2009 Regional Groups are the future of the League: A number of regional groups had been successfully established and were well supported. Members were encouraged to attend one of these groups or start a new group in their area.

In this way, League members could continue to meet up with Guy's trained nurses and the League could live on, albeit in a different format. The League website would also continue to disseminate information and circulate news.

2010 Lead up to July 10th: In the 2009 Journal, members were told they could begin to apply for tickets from 18th January 2010. Three of the Officers had volunteered to co-ordinate the ticket sales and the thought was that applications would trickle in from the opening date. However the Officers were amazed to find that three carrier bags full of forms had been received by 19th January. Cream teas (200 tickets) were sold out the first morning and before all these initial applications could be processed, the 700 lunch tickets had also been snapped up.

Feeling that to disappoint so many people who had applied so early was unthinkable a new lunch venue was sought and found at the Hop Exchange, a restored hop warehouse ten minutes walk away.

Guy's agreed to provide another 12 lunches and Glaziers another 40 so with the new venue of 250 over 1000 people would be provided with lunch. Applications continued to flood in and lunch tickets were sold out within a couple of weeks.

The planning for the auction of memorabilia also took up much time and effort for the Officers and other helpers. Over the years the League had acquired a surprising number of artefacts and other items. TW Gaze, an Auctioneers in Suffolk very kindly agreed to value some of the items without charge.

It was found that some WW1 medals sent to the League after the death of their owners were very valuable. Very few women had served their country in WW1 and most of those who did were nurses. As a consequence few medals were awarded to women during that time, making those who were fairly unique and thus more valuable.

One of these nurses was Mabel Chittock who trained at Guy's from 1900–03 and was a sister there 1904–05. In WW1 she was awarded a Military medal for bravery in the field, a Red Cross Medal 1st class and the Order of St John of Jerusalem.

There were a large number of items not suitable to auction so it was decided to also have a sale of items on the day.

As the day drew nearer, last minute meetings took place with the Cathedral, the outside caterers and the Guy's Hospitality and Logistics Departments who were exceptionally helpful and supportive.

June 2010: A last minute hitch: Tickets were sold, table plans sorted, leaflets, menus and service sheets were printed and the organisers were beginning to feel confident that everything was in place for the day. Out of the blue and with less than a month to go the League received news that the Hop Exchange would no longer be available as the site had been the subject of a compulsory order from Network Rail and no further events could take place there. This meant that 250 people would be without lunch. It seemed impossible that a new venue could be found in such a short time. However the caterers from the Hop Exchange managed to book Vinopolis, a spectacular venue near to Southwark Cathedral. The caterers were more than helpful, underwriting the extra hire and food prices, paying to inform diners of the new venue and for new menus to be printed.

July 10th 2010 The Final AGM: a detailed account of this can be found in Chapter 11.

August 2010, League President dies: Pam Jefferies, League President since 2007 died after a two year illness. Pam had continued to take an active part in League affairs until April 2010 but was too unwell to attend the July 10th celebrations and died on August 13th. Pam had been involved with the League for over 30 years. She was editor of the Journal from 1976–77 and returned later as a past and present nurse representative. She was voted President-Elect in 2003 and became President in 2007.

Pam Jefferies

September 22nd 2010 Final Council meeting: The 362nd and last meeting of the Council took place with 22 Council members attending. After tea and a commemorative cake they were treated to an initial showing of the DVD of July 10th which received much appreciative feedback.

Above: Chairman Alison Russell and Mavis Fabling cut the cake; Right: The Cake

December 2010: The Benevolent and Scholarship Funds were handed over to the Charity for future management.

Archives. Previously many of the League records and photos had been stored at the London Metropolitan Archives (LMA) in Clerkenwell, London facilitated by Brenda Faulkner who had become Archive Representative on Council.

The remaining records, including minutes of meetings from 1957, the Nursing Guides and all the Journals from 1966 were given to the LMA to provide a comprehensive record of the League covering 110 years.

December 31st 2010: The League finally closes.

Kneeler to commemorate the closure of the League made by June Blackwell

CHAPTER NINE

League Leaders:
1900–2006

Dame Sarah Ann Swift

Dame Sarah Ann Swift
Founder of the League
The First Honorary Secretary 1900–09
Member of the League 1900–37

Sarah Swift, 'founder of the League' was a private diminutive person, she was only 4' 10" tall, who shunned publicity but she was one of the most influential, respected nurses of her day. She was a leading figure on the issue of nurse registration, promoted an early version of a pension fund for nurses, and founded the College of Nursing, later the R.C.N. Her strategy was to work with the powerful medical and hospital authorities of the time to achieve improvements for nursing and this made her unpopular with some of her contemporaries who thought nurses should lead on everything.

So respected was she that she was called out of retirement at the outbreak of WW1, and appointed Matron in Chief of the Joint War Committee of the St John Ambulance Association and the British Red Cross. She was responsible for 6000 nurses as well as the VADs who acted as nursing assistants. Following the war she was awarded the Dame Grand Cross of the Order of the British Empire.

Dame Sarah was a member of Guy's Nurses' League until her death and kept up her association with the League and the Hospital, attending many AGMs, taking the Chair and presenting prizes and medals. She was elected a lifelong League Vice President after her retirement from Guy's. Her last public appearance was at the coronation of George VI in 1936. Shortly after she became seriously ill and died within weeks.

In 1903, at the League AGM, it was stated:

> 'If Matron intended to make a thing a success, they could take it for granted that it would be carried out'.[39]

This could be her epitaph.

Sir Henry Cosmo Orme Bonsor
First Chairman of the League 1900–10
Vice President 1910–29

Sir Cosmo Bonsor was born in 1848 at Great Bookham, near Dorset. After education at Eton he joined the family brewing firm. In 1898 he became the first chairman of Watney, Combe and Reid, the largest brewing company of its day, and also chairman of the South Eastern Railway. Later he was also a director of the Bank of England and the Northern Assurance Company and chairman of the Income Tax Commissioners for the City of London. He was also the Conservative MP for Wimbledon from 1885–1900.

Henry Cosmo Bonsor was Treasurer of Guy's Hospital from 1896–1909 and turned the hospital's financial position around. He became the first Chairman of the Nurses' League when it was formed in 1900. He was a great supporter of the League, and a great humanitarian. Much loved by the members, he is remembered to this day via the Sir Cosmo & Lady Mabel Scholarship Fund.

Sir Cosmo Bonsor

Lady Mabel Bonsor

Lady Mabel Bonsor
First President of the League 1900–44
Chairman 1923–39

Mabel Brand was born in Surrey in 1864. She married Henry Cosmo Bonsor following the death of his first wife, Emily in 1882. When her husband became Guy's Treasurer in 1896 she began an association with Guy's that lasted until her death in 1944. When the Guy's Nurses' League was founded she became the President and took an active role in League affairs. She was particularly interested in The Cottage at Honor Oak Park, decorating and furnishing the nurses' bedrooms.

She supported all the clubs and societies; particularly music, drama and the sports clubs and provided prizes for the needlework, painting and photography competitions. She was very involved with the patients and was a frequent visitor to Naaman ward taking magazines, chocolates and flowers for the patients. She also showed great interest in the welfare of the domestic staff and porters.

Lady Mabel Bonsor was much loved by many at Guy's and especially by League members. When she died in 1944 the League set up a scholarship fund in her name that was later merged with the Cosmo Bonsor Fund.

For a number of years in the early days of the League, the Bonsors invited all the nursing staff to a yearly party at their splendid country house at Kingswood Warren in Surrey.

A typical trip was described in the Obituary to Mabel Bonsor included in the 1944 Nursing Supplement:

> '. . . As many nurses as could be spared (in uniform in those days!) went down to Kingswood in a special saloon train which Sir Cosmo, as Chairman of the London and Brighton and South Coast, now the Southern Railway, provided; the drive up from the station in wagonettes and brakes, the lovely grounds, games, music, a pony to ride, and such unlimited strawberries and cream . . . our gracious host and hostess moving among their guests . . . making sure that every guest found enjoyment.[40]

Other members of the Bonsor family have also been associated with the League in more recent times. Lady Reginald Bonsor was an Honorary member in the 1950s and Miss Brand, a niece and goddaughter of Lady Mabel served on Council also as an Honorary member.

Louisa Haughton
Honorary Secretary 1909–17
Member of the League 1900–54

Louisa Haughton

Louisa Haughton had the daunting task of following Sarah Swift as Matron. Quiet and unassuming but with a broad outlook on life and a great sense of humour, she soon demonstrated her own qualities and personality.

Emily MacManus described her first meeting with Miss Haughton:

> *'There she was, our new Matron. Miss L.V. Haughton, walking beneath the plane trees in the Park* (at Guy's).

> *We met face to face. She wore a long black frock, a white apron with a short bib, and a rounded white cap. She never wore a peak to her cap. With her deep set eyes in a small oval face she looked to me, like some watchful squirrel – and then she smiled, and her whole face lit up with humour. That was the key-note of Miss Haughton's character. A high ideal, a becoming gravity in repose, a steady devotion to the work that lay in front of her, whatever it might be'.*[41]

In November 1916 Miss Haughton was suddenly struck by a life threatening illness and had to resign from her post as Matron. Her resignation was described as an irreparable loss to Guy's; and she would always be remembered for her gentle dignity, her culture, her humour and understanding. She eventually retired to Bridport in Dorset where she died in 1954 aged 85.

Margaret Hogg, C.B.E
Honorary Secretary 1917–27
Member of the League 1905–75

Calm, practical and efficient, Margaret Hogg, Assistant Matron at the time, had to pick up the reins when Louisa Haughton fell ill and she was appointed as Matron in 1918.

In the post war years she soon brought the hospital back to normality and under her guidance nursing at Guy's continued to develop.

During her time as Matron, the cottage had a major upgrade and the clubs, particularly tennis and swimming were most successful.

She retired in 1927 but continued to maintain her contact with the Nurses' League and later was a Vice President. In her 90's she lived in Worthing and in 1975 shortly before her death she was visited by League members who reported that she was completely deaf and communicated by printing words on a large sheet of paper, however she enjoyed pottering about at home and loved to reminisce.

She died on October 25th 1975

Margaret Hogg, Matron 1917–27

In her 93rd year in 1972

Emily MacManus
Honorary Secretary 1927–46
President 1957–78
Member of the League 1908–78

Emily Elvira Primrose MacManus was probably the most revered and loved of the Guy's Matrons and League Honorary Secretaries.

It was written in the Journal when she died that she would have been recognised as an outstanding person in whatever walk of life she had chosen to follow.

Happily she chose nursing and there followed a life time dedicated to the care of others.

She was known for her humanity and insight into the needs of others, especially those in distress. Frank and down to earth she always called a spade a spade but was fair

Emily MacManus

and un-judgmental. She had a great sense of humour and a ready wit.

She was a tower of strength and an inspiring leader during WW2 when she was Sector Matron of the South East of England.

Emily was a League member for over 70 years, almost three quarters of the life of the League. A member since 1908 she was still attending League meetings over 65 years later as President. Betty Herbert's new title under the Salmon re-organisation was Principal Nursing Officer and on introducing her at the 1972 AGM, Emily, a little confused with the new terminology, called her 'Chief Petty Officer' – I imagine with tongue firmly in cheek!

Dorothy Smith, C.B.E.
Honorary Secretary 1946–53
President 1979–82,
Member of the League 1916–91

Kitty Bulleid
Chairman 1947–57,
Vice Chairman 1974–86,
Member of the League 1918–86

Jean Addison (later Mrs Recknell),
Honorary Secretary 1953–62,
Member of the League 1930–90

Ann Johnson
Honorary Secretary
1962–69

Linda Titley, Honorary Secretary 1969–71,
Chairman 1969–74, Vice-Chairman
1974–99, Member of the League 1933–99

Florence Taylor, Chairman 1957–69,
Vice Chairman 1969–71,
Member of the League 1916–71

Miss Florence Taylor, affectionately known by many as Sister 'Flo' was a great League character.

In her Obituary, written by no less a person than Emily MacManus, she was described as *'an inspired teacher, a disciplinarian in the best sense of the world, with a keen sense of humour and kind and encouraging towards her young students'.*[42]

Florence trained from 1916–19 and became Holiday Sister and Night Sister in 1927. She first appeared on Council as the Debating Society representative in 1927 and re-appeared in 1930 as the Photographic rep, a year in which she was also appointed as Assistant Sister Tutor. From 1934–52 she was the Library Representative.

Sister Flo loved to travel and toured Europe extensively in her little car. During the war she sped round the Kentish Lanes to the six scattered units of the School of Nursing, occasionally dodging incendiary bombs, to lecture or counsel the student nurses. At the end of the war she helped re-establish the School of Nursing at Guy's and introduced the Block System of training, the first in the UK.

She retired to Blackheath in South London and kept her close association with Guy's and the League, being chairman for twelve years. She died on St Georges Day 1971.

Doreen Sinclair-Brown, M.B.E.
President 1984–89
Chairman 1974–79
Vice Chairman 1980–83
Member of the League 1938–2000

Barbara Stevenson (Stevie)
Honorary Assistant Secretary 1976–78,
Chairman 1979–83, Honorary Secretary 1984–95,
Journal Editor 1980–93, Vice President 1995–2010,
League member 1943–2010

Stevie is a legend in her time as she has served the League for so many years in so many capacities. When she eventually retired as an Officer in 1995 she was asked to reminisce about her time with the League.

> 'I retired from my appointment as Senior Nursing Officer for Midwifery in October 1975 but happily was able to keep up my links with the hospital on being invited to become Assistant Honorary Secretary of the League. I received my induction into the mysteries of League administration from Joan Blackburn who was retiring from the post. At that time we worked in an "office" on the 1st floor of Guy's House, above Matron's Office. The room was little more than a broom cupboard; certainly only two people could fit into it at any one time. With help from Jean Baker we kept the register of members and the index cards up to date as well as coping with the subscriptions. In 1979 I was promoted as Chairman for the next five years and during that time I also took on the editorship of the Journal, which I carried on until 1993.
>
> On completing my term as Chairman in 1984, I became Honorary Secretary. All my wearing of different hats has lasted over 19 years during which time, apart from holidays, I have been to Guy's every week and when necessary, such as the great annual mailing of the Journals, more frequently. Just in case you think I am making this commitment sound like hard labour, I have thoroughly enjoyed the experience and feel privileged that I have been able to keep up my connections with Guy's for so long after my retirement'.[43]

Betty Herbert (née White) was the last of the great Matrons of Guy's and the last Matron to be Honorary Secretary of the League.

She has given many years of service to the League in a variety of roles and steered it and the hospital through much change and upheaval. When Betty retired as 'Matron' in 1981 she carried on as Honorary Secretary for another three years when her successor felt she did not have time to take on this role.

There followed periods as Chairman and President during more difficult times when the future of Guy's and the League was in doubt.

In the last few years Betty was unable to attend League meetings due to ill health but she always kept in touch with the League and phoned the Honorary Secretary before each Council meeting, giving her apologies and sending her best wishes to all.

A special message from her commemorating the League was read out at the celebratory service in Southwark Cathedral on July 10th 2010.

Betty Herbert
Honorary Secretary 1972–83, Chairman 1984–88, President 1989–95,
Vice President 1996–2010, League member 1942–2010

Mavis Fabling
Honorary Secretary 1995–96, Journal Editor 1994–2001,
Privileged Member 2003–10

Mavis is another great League character. She first appeared on Council as a student nurse representing the Nurses Representative Council in 1958.

She returned again in 1972 as Library representative.

Mavis wrote a narrative of an imaginary Guy's nurse for the commemorative exhibition on display in the 1996 celebrations. This depicted the life of a Guy's nurse through the ages, since the founding of the hospital. This narrative was published in the book 'Nursing at Guy's' in 1997.[44] Mavis was a memorable editor of eight editions of the League Journal.

Joan Page
Chairman 1989–92,
League member 1949–2010

Margo Lamb
President 1996–2000,
League member 1956–2010

*Betsy Morley
Chairman 1993–97,
President 2001–03,
League member 1959–2010*

Betsy was the first Chairman to also hold a current clinical post.

*Lisa Burnapp
Chairman 1998–2003,
League member 1985–2010*

Lisa was the youngest ever Chairman.

Sally Hudson
Honorary Secretary 1996–2001,
League member 1967–2010

Vron Taylor
President 2004–06,
League member 1959–2010

Now follows a few pages of photos including just some of the League members and Honorary members you may remember.

The others are some I have acquired during my research for this book; some do not have direct League connections, but that I felt I had to share them with you.

Some well-loved faces for many of you

Agnes 'Polly' Perkins was a much loved Assistant Matron in the 1950s and 1960s.

Sister Nora Relihan 'Reli' who devoted herself to Guy's patients for 50 years with never a day's sick leave.

Audrey Crump 'Crumpy' A dedicated children's nurse and League legend. She sat on Council for several terms and was voted an Honorary Vice Chairman in 1997.

Muriel Theisen 'Thei' another League legend. A Guy's District Health Visitor from 1958–78; who worked from 8 a.m.–7 p.m. helping local families. After her retirement she contributed much to the League as Honorary Assistant Secretary.

Some well known Honorary Members

Sandra Carnall came to Guy's in 1962 and was still doing some consultancy work for the Trust in 2009. She has contributed much to Council with all her detailed knowledge of Guy's and played many parts in the pantomime.

Rachel Townsin worked in Nursing Administration and helped in the League Office for 30 years.

Lydia Franks sat on Council as the representative of 'A Friend in Need'.

Eddie Rowe a Special Trustee of Guy's and former Mayor of Bermondsey, with a generous nature who contributed wise advice to Council.

I am unable to identify what this shield was being presented for though it is likely to have been for tennis or swimming in the 1920s. The recipients look so pleased to receive it!

A delightful picture of three well known tutors from the 1930s–1950s.

Simon Hughes with friends at the cocktail party on July 10th.
Simon was one of the special guests at the Cathedral Service.
The local MP, he has close connections with Guy's, particularly in leading
the Save Guy's Campaign and has been a guest speaker at League AGMs.

CHAPTER TEN

The Nursing Guides and the Journals

The Nursing Guides

The first Nursing Guide was published in 1902 and there were to be thirteen more editions every few years until the final edition in 1960.

The purpose of the Guide was explained in the Preface of the first edition:

> 'The original object in view in the preparation of this work was simply to provide a Hand-book of the Nurses' League of Guy's Hospital, and a Register of the Nurses trained at this Institution. In the course of this preparation the desirability was recognised of including a section which would be of general service to the community. This has been done, and the first pages of the book constitute a Nursing Guide, which those aspiring to enter the Nursing Profession may in particular consult with advantage'.[45]

The Guides contained comprehensive information for those aspiring to nursing or those already in the profession.

In 1904: The first section describes the benefits of nursing as a profession:

> 'Hospital nursing is a profession that has been for the last twenty or thirty years very attractive to young women who are either seeking for a way to earn their own living, or for some definite work to fill up what would otherwise be a half-idle life. The attractions are manifold. To mention only a few – there is the satisfaction to the learners that they are engaged in business that may be reckoned on to support them

comfortably, unless their health fails, until their working days are over;
and there is the delight of constantly learning something new, for the
variety in nursing is infinite; and not by any means to be forgotten,
there is the pleasant society of girls of their own age, with interests in
the same direction and ambitions of the same sort'.[46]

Later it describes the requirements, physical, mental and moral for a probationer:

'She must be between 23 and 32 years old. As to stature, extreme
shortness or slightness of figure is a drawback, so she should not
measure less than five feet two inches in height, nor be much under
eight stone in weight, when wearing ordinary clothes . . . Her health
must be unexceptional, for if there is weak spot in any part of her – a
delicate chest, tendency to varicose veins, nervous excitability, or what
not – life in a hospital will surely bring it out. Her sense of sight, smell
and hearing must be perfect . . . .

Her manner must be quiet and self-possessed, neither slow and
lackadaisical, nor bustling and noisy . . .

Perfect neatness in dress is required of every probationer. Missing
buttons, torn aprons, and slipshod shoes augur badly for her future
career; for if she cannot keep herself tidy, how can she ensure the order
of the ward?'[46]

No mention of caring or job satisfaction!

Later in the book was a section on urine testing – this was long before a single testing stick could detect most abnormalities, and five pages on poison antidotes and treatment, including for arsenic, belladonna, caustic potash, laudanum, nitric acid, strychnine and turpentine.

There was also a large section containing useful recipes for the sickroom for, at this time, nurses were expected to cook nutritious and appropriate food for their patients. Recipes included those for: Beef tea, broths, bland fish dishes, egg recipes, various jellies and gruels.

The League section of the Guide included a list of Patrons and Patronesses, the Council, and the rules and regulations for the League as well as the various clubs and societies. After that there was news of the hospital, appointments, and the AGM, followed by the register.

CONTENTS.

The Guide was a hard backed book and continued in this format for the next three editions when it was decided that as the information in the nursing guide changed little it was not cost effective to send it out annually. In its place the Annual Supplement and Matron's Christmas letter were introduced.

The twelfth 'Guide' was printed in 1937. The contents page had not changed a lot in the intervening years but some of the advice and information had been updated.

The section on the Nursing Profession for example no longer gives advice on nursing as a career but describes the current situation in nursing.

> *'The nursing profession is in a state of healthy unrest and transition. Big questions are at stake, and energetic leaders are striving to settle them on progressive and sound lines . . .*
>
> *Organised nursing services are still in their infancy, and wholehearted and thoughtful support is needed for those pioneers who are trying to bring about reforms in the face of great difficulties . . .*
>
> *Surely no profession offers wider or more adventurous fields of service both home and abroad. Never were pioneers and educated women of independent thought more needed than today in the nursing profession. May the spirit of service rather than consideration of self be the strong incentive for the younger generation to lead them into fresh fields'.*[47]

World War Two then intervened and the next 'Guide', in revised and updated form did not appear until 1950.

It opened with a history of nursing at Guy's from 1725–1945, much of which was taken from Miss MacManus' Christmas letters from 1927 onwards.

At this time the register still contained detailed information about the members:

Miss MacManus' entry for 1950 was one of the longest:

MacManus Emily E.P., C.B.E., The Cottage, Cassington, near Eynsham, Oxon and Carrickbarrett Lodge, Boffenaun, Ballina, Co. Mayo, Eire. Student nurse, Guy's Hosp., 1908 to 1911. Sister, Kasr el Aini Hosp., Cairo, 1912. Private nursing in Cairo, to 1913. Holiday Sister, Guy's Hosp., 3 months, 1913. Theatre Sister. King's Lynn Hosp., to May 1914. Sister, Guy's Hosp., to 1915. Staff nurse and Sister, Civil Hospital Reserve, France, to Dec 1918. Asst. Matron, Guy's Hosp., to May 1922. Asst. for Food Experiment for Med. Research Council, to Aug. 1923. Matron, Bristol Royal Infirmary, to March, 1927. Matron, Guy's Hosp. to 1946. Cert. S.C.M. Mentioned in Dispatches, Nov 1917, King's Jubilee Medal, 1935. S.R.N.[48]

The fourteenth and last edition of the Guide was issued in 1960.

The preface explained that in view of the great increase in nursing and scientific publications the Council of the League considered that these sections had out-worn their usefulness and they had decided to omit them.

The personal information in the register was also amended and included only the name and address of members, with no career details.

At this time, the League was struggling to fund the cost of the Handbook and League members were canvassed as to the strategy for funding future publications. 537 members expressed the wish that the Handbook and Register should only be available on application. 249 members supported an increase in subscriptions.

Despite the majority decision, the Council decided that it was important that all members continued to receive the Handbook, so it raised subscriptions to cover the cost.

The cost of the Guides was defrayed by advertising, some of which companies are still well known to this day:

Some examples of adverts from 1904–10:

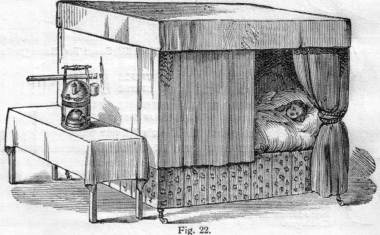

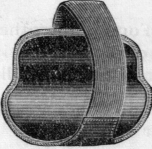

The Supplements and Matron's Christmas Letter

The Nursing Guide Supplements and Matron's Christmas letter were sent out together from approximately 1910.

The supplement mainly comprised the League information section that occupied the end of the Nursing Guide. It began with the membership of Council, then promotions and new appointments, obituaries, an account of the AGM, prize and medal winners, financial accounts and change of addresses or details of new members rather than a full register.

There were also reports of the various clubs and societies. From 1913 the announcement of member's marriages was added and in 1914 details of births to members were also included.

Occasionally a special or significant event was reported in the Supplement.

The 1914 edition contained the experiences and reflections of nurses serving abroad in the war. Sister Kiddle, wrote from Versailles where she was based in a converted first class hotel which still had luxurious carpets on the floor:

> 'We are beginning to realise what a truly dreadful game war is. Why should a civilised people stoop to such a means of settling disputes? To see the way these men are brought along in train loads lying on straw makes me shiver. Imagine fractured femurs and far worse jostling along for two or three days in such a state.
>
> . . . in less than two hours nearly three hundred poor fellows are admitted. The whole process is too awful and too real to describe . . . . Then came the great task of getting them undressed and into bed. They were all so dirty, tired and hungry, and some so ill, even apart from their injuries. They had been marching for days on practically nothing, and then had a hard fight at the end of it. Some arrived with hardly anything on: one man had half a coat and a hat, one leg had been amputated on the field, and he was looking awful, but so pleased to be put comfy in bed and get a hot drink, and, above all, a smoke. He got on splendidly for the first twenty-four hours, and then the following morning his jaw was stiff and he had one or two nasty spasms, – and you can guess the rest'.[49]

Miss Kiddle was later awarded the Royal Red Cross medal, 1st class.

Each year there was an account of Christmas in the Hospital, when all the staff made every effort to ensure the patients enjoyed the festivities and the wards competed with each other to achieve the best decorations.

> *The wards looked very pretty with their coloured lampshades and decorations. Astley Cooper with its Alpine Scene, horse race, merry-go-rounds, swingboats and football match, represented outdoor sports. Cornelius had almond blossoms; Dorcas, scenes from Alice in Wonderland; Luke was a country village, with its church, village store, railway and bus. Patience and Samaritan was Rainbowland. Naaman represented an Underground Railway Station, the whole of the Ward being draped, so as to give one the idea of looking down a long tunnel which disappeared round the corner. Christopher had Hampstead Heath as its setting. Mary had laburnum, wisteria, paper parasols and Chinese lanterns; and Queen was very gay with its quantities of scarlet Cape gooseberries'.[50]*

In 1930 there was a description of the Garden Party at the Cottage, which was frequently dogged by bad weather:

> *'The Annual Garden Party and Re-Union of the Guy's Hospital Nurses' League was held at the Nurses' Cottage. Honor Oak Park, on Wednesday June 18th, 1930, but the afternoon was marred by a torrential downpour of rain, thunder and lightning. For the first half-hour after their arrival the guests were able to enjoy the garden, which looked at its best . . . A tennis match between the Nursing and Administrative Staff and other garden games had been arranged, and a band from St Dunstan's began a musical programme at 3 o'clock. At 3.30 the thunderstorm broke, and everyone fled to the Cottage; the food which was in the tent was rescued during a lull in the storm, and tea was served by gaslight to cheerful crowds sitting in every available corner in the sitting room, hall and stairs'.[51]*

World War Two warranted particular comment in the Supplement:

The foreword in 1941 Supplement wrote:

> *'It is twelve months since the last Christmas supplement was sent to members of the Guy's Hospital Past and Present Nurses' League. How quickly the time seems to have gone; it brings the much desired end of the war so much nearer.*

In this space of time much has happened in Europe, and yet, far from being nearer his goal, Hitler seems to be faced with the prospects of an unpleasant winter in Russia. We may wonder what our part in the next year will be'.[52]

In the corresponding Christmas letter Emily MacManus wrote:

'Once again, A Happy Christmas! Never before has Thomas Guy's "family" been scattered so far afield – from the snows and hot springs of Iceland to the snows and hot springs of New Zealand; from Australia's vast territories to Canada's wide spaces; from the Middle East to the Far East; from North Africa to South Africa; from South America to the South Atlantic and the South Pacific Isles – you are there, the embodiment of Britain.

Wherever you are, Guy's sends its daughters a message of remembrance and encouragement and affection'.[53]

In 1942 the Supplement was not published due to war time restrictions on the use of paper but Matron's Christmas letter continued. Emily MacManus told her readers of the garden she had organised in the ruins of the Superintendent's House at Guy's:

'At Guy's itself I have a garden in the evacuated basement of the Superintendents House. I owe gratitude to the Heavy Rescue Squad in the Borough who, as part of their excavation practice work, came along with their van full of tools. Nothing was too difficult for them. I felt that given half a chance they would have rebuilt Guy's!

They moved water tanks, built a duck pond for me, got up the concrete cellar floors and paving slabs, and exposed the earth that had been covered by the building for over two hundred years. As a beginning we were able to grow extra greens for the patients – peas, beans, lettuces, spring onions for tea, some marrows and ridge cucumbers – and we got second and third prizes in the horticultural show in Walworth Road.

Chickens, ducks and rabbits thrive in the two gardens behind the Matron's House and the netball ground, and provide eggs and a little extra and welcome "white meat" for the light diet patients, and, in addition, valuable manure for the garden. So you see, we really are agriculturalists'.[54]

In 1953, Matron Dorothy Smith attended the Coronation of Queen Elizabeth II, and recalled her memories in the Supplement:

'Although the doors of the Abbey were closed when Big Ben had sounded the hour of half past eight, and a long time intervened before the great event, a dull moment was impossible. The sight of the guests of all sorts and conditions slowly making their way up the magnificent carpet which spread from end to end of the building was, in itself, an unforgettable experience . . .

. . . When all the lights were turned on, the Abbey seemed to resemble the interior of some enchanted cave, while it might almost be said that the lighting was equal to the sun at noon day . . .

Before the Queen's procession was due, there was an unrehearsed incident – white coated attendants came with carpet sweepers, brooms and brushes. Even then one of them was not satisfied, but picked up by hand the difficult pieces, as housewives have done in their homes from time immemorial . . .

. . . After the service was ended came the great moment for those seated in the nave. The same measured progress paced westward till, to the massed singing of "God Save the Queen", Her Majesty appeared, wearing the massively glittering Imperial crown and great purple and ermine robe. With the music breaking into "Land of Hope and Glory", there came into our vision the lissome figure moving so gracefully and easily, not withstanding the great burdens and glories of queenship upon her'.[55]

In 1955 a 'News Sheet' was introduced into the Supplement. The increasing numbers of League members working abroad were writing of their experiences and these were also published in the Supplement. Lydia Bishop and Joyce McNiven went for a three year tour to Malaya and Lydia wrote of the exceptional birth rate which resulted in almost 20,000 deliveries a year at their hospital.

There followed articles from Johannesburg, Nigeria, Canada and the USA, Rio de Janeiro, India, the West Indies and many others.

Phyllis Buckley wrote from the Zambezi Valley:

'The Zambezi Valley seems quite out of this turbulent world, parts of it resemble a peaceful English park, with massive trees, luxuriant grass and very rich soil.

When, however, a lioness, sleek and majestic, walked across the road, we realised it really was Africa. She hesitated, gave us a penetrating *stare, then walked slowly on. Behind her trotted two frisky little cubs. The cubs were very interested in the car and walked round several times sniffing the tyres. A few minutes later the lioness came back to see where they were. She cuffed the smaller cub over the head with a tremendous paw and the whole family moved off into the veld together'.*[56]

Stories from overseas continued to flood in and in 1961 members at home were also encouraged to send their news to the League.

'It is a pity that the News Sheet mainly refers to trainees abroad as there must be any number in this country who are holding important posts, or undertaking work of an unusual nature which their friends would be interested to hear about. News of older members would also be welcome'.[57]

The Supplements and Christmas letters continued to be sent every Christmas until 1964 when the Matron suggested that the League consider a more modern, attractive magazine to replace them and the Handbooks.

A small sub-committee of Council was formed to discuss this proposal.

The Journal

The Council sub-committee supported a new look magazine. They agreed that the contents should be decided by the editor but should include such items as: Matron's letter, Treasurer's report, Secretary's report, reports on clubs etc., original articles on current trends, letters from home and abroad and births, deaths, marriages etc. They proposed that advertisements be sought to help defray the expense; that the cost be borne by the League; that the editor be Matron or someone appointed by her and that a paid secretary be employed to assist with the typing etc.

An editorial committee under Beryl Warne was appointed with a view to the publication in 1965. This was a little ambitious and an update to Council in May 1965 reported that a format had been decided and printers identified, though there was delay mainly due to the difficulty of updating the register. The cost was likely to be £415 for 3,000 copies, with some of it defrayed by advertisements, although in the event only one company was found. The Hospital Endowments Fund contributed £100 towards the printing cost.

The First Journal

The first new look Journal was sent to members in May 1966, with Myra Calvert as Editor, following the resignation of Miss Warne.

The first edition coincided with the arrival of a new Hospital Chairman, Lord Robens of Woldingham who wrote a welcome in the Journal.

> *'I am delighted to welcome the first issue of the Journal of the Guy's Nurses' League because it will be an admirable vehicle for communication . . . I hope that this new venture will help to weld together more firmly all who are associated with nursing at Guy's'.*[58]

The new Journal retained many of the aspects of the old Supplements including Hospital News, a resume of the AGM and financial reports and news from members at home and abroad.

Innovations in the Journal were a list of Sisters in Office and articles of interest from members and others. The subject of one of the latter was the Intensive Treatment Unit, itself an innovation at the time, together with comprehensive news of the New Guy's, with illustrations, from Harry Burfoot, Clerk to the Governors.

Each year there were reports of the remaining clubs and societies, the swimming and tennis club, the music society and the library.

For the first copy in 1966, the editors were delighted to receive a diary written by an in patient in December 1892 and excerpts of this were included:

> *'Monday 26th December, 1892. Commenced this day by reading ten hymns and two chapters of Genesis . . . Washed by Nurse Holmes at 8am.*
>
> *Some short time back, I am informed, the nurses had a General Strike, My opinion – they need strike. The hours are far too long; many of the nurses commence at 6 am and finish at 8.30 pm; making it a long day . . . They have to attend chapel several times a week. They were lately informed not to put buttons in the collecting bags. But nurses, like others, are full of fun and up to all kinds of amusements . . . The night nurses are barred from seeing any of the fun this day. They have to go to bed – and fancy being locked in their bedrooms! . . .*

All kinds of refreshments brought round after dinner. All those who were able to get up were dressed and carried up to the front. Those who could not get up had to lay and smoke their long clay pipe in bed'.

'28.12.92. Second week in Guy's Hospital. This day being one of the thickest fogs I have ever seen. Lights full on and yet dark. Could not see to read. We all knew what aching eyes were this day'.[59]

An attempt was made to brighten up the first Journal with photographs, including the Guy's arms, the Colonnade in springtime and the front of the hospital in summer.

Guy's Hospital, summer 1965, from the 1966 Journal

The greatest challenge was the updating of the register of members which was published in the Journal annually.

From the start the League struggled with the cost of an annual Journal and in 1972 it was decided to publish the register every two years to save money. In 1973 again as a cost cutting measure, the list of Sisters in post was omitted and in 1985, the size of the print was reduced also to reduce costs.

The League was most grateful to the Hospital Governors and the Friends of Guy's who gave very generous donations towards the printing of the Journal.

By 1976 the enthusiasm for writing from 'home and abroad' had somewhat abated but this meant that more of each members news could be printed which made this section far more interesting.

It also encouraged more in depth articles from members that gave some insight into the difficulties and challenges faced when living or working abroad.

In 1971, Elizabeth Searle went to Ghana with her husband and children. Her article commences:

> 'Doctor! Snake, snake' Joseph, our steward, called out excitedly. A large black spitting cobra lay curled on the doorstep in the twilight. A few swift blows with a heavy stick and Joseph was able to display his trophy to Timothy (3 years) and Rebecca (1 and a half). Life for them and for us in Ghana was certainly never dull.[60]

Wendy Myers was one of the most prolific writers on working abroad and she sent articles from Matabeleland, Northern Sudan, the Himalayas, West Nepal, Gorom Gorom in Upper Volta and Munda in the Solomon Islands. Four months after her arrival in Munda in 1973, circumstances found her in the position of Acting Matron:

> 'Now, the night calls were more demanding than "There's a delivery" and with cautious fumbling hands I would put up "drips", suture knife wounds or take malaria slides from someone in the clutches of a rigor.
>
> As part of my work I learned how to do Ventouse extractions, give anaesthetics and do intra-peritoneal transfusion'.[61]

Later she explains her own rather disgusting way of telling how acclimatised were people to working in Munda, by judging how they reacted when bugs, which were everywhere, got into their food.

> 'First stage: they throw it all away.
>
> Second stage: they remove the bug and eat the rest of their food.
>
> Third stage: they push the bug to one side and carry on.
>
> Fourth stage: they eat the bug with the food.
>
> Final stage: they suspect that there is something wrong with the food when there is no bug in it'.[61]

In 1977, Wendy, now qualified as a Health Visitor accepted a post for the Save the Children Fund in Nepal. She tells a story that illustrates the sort of difference members like her could make:

> *'Some people are literally tied to their surroundings through poverty. One afternoon found us tramping over steep, stony hillside to answer a "call for help" from a father who described his daughter as being "very ill". The little girl was lying in a pool of blood and faeces, too weak to move. While treating her, I asked the man why his child (who had been ill for two weeks) had not been brought to clinic. "None of us could take time off from our work" came the reply. After spending a hour with the patient, coaxing her to drink, cleaning her up, and explaining medicines and the importance of fluids to her father, we called to see a neighbour's daughter who was also "very ill". The child was lying in the house alone in the same state as the first. After an extensive search, the parents were located and fetched. When I explained the seriousness of the girl's condition, the father simply shrugged and said: "Yes, we accept that she might die, but if we don't do our work in the fields now, the whole family will starve later.*
>
> *However that day did end on a promising note, because the father of the first girl spent a long time teaching what he had just learned (ie. the care of a patient with amoebic dysentery) to his neighbours'.*[62]

The good news is that both girls survived.

One of the most regular contributors among the members was Mary Foreman, who lives and worked in Italy. Her first articles were written in the early 1980s and she contributed almost every year, including the last Journal published in 2009.

Other favoured topics for articles were reminiscences of years gone by and the experience of members returning to nursing after many years absence, managing a home and raising a family.

Marny Hallam, had trained in 1935 and returned to nursing in 1965 after the sudden death of her husband. She was interviewed by Matron for a Home Sister's post at a London Teaching Hospital and later heard from a colleague that Matron's comment was: *'I think we had better take this one: at least she seems a bit more with it than the one I saw yesterday'.*[63]

Later she moved to a local seaside hospital where she was allocated to the Private Patients floor, having been told to watch her step as: *Sister doesn't want you and, like me, she doesn't like teaching hospital types and doctor's wives, and you are both'.*[63]

In 1980, Barbara Watson took a return to nursing course. She learnt many things:

> . . .*'That things sterile arrived in packages, both big and small; that one discarded syringes and needles after use! One no longer went through the ritual of "laying up" trolleys, one no longer "boiled up" the ward sterilizer'.*[64]

In the 1978 Journal, Dorothy Norman looked back to her days as a student nurse in 1934:

> *'I was working in the Private Ward in Hunt's House . . . Mrs Moore, aged about 57 years, was in my charge, and had been admitted for gastric investigations. Soon I learned with much excitement that she was Queen Mary's housekeeper . . . . As time passed, she gave me glimpses of life in Buckingham Palace: the amusing punctuality races between the King and Queen to reach the breakfast table first at 9am . . . If the Queen had a cold, Mrs Moore wanted to send breakfast up to her room, but that was considered a weakness in the Queen's eyes and she always refused'.*[65]

When Mrs Moore returned to work she invited Dorothy to a magnificent tour of Buckingham Palace.

In 1980, Margery Poyser wrote of her interview for children's nursing in 1921:

> *'I was nineteen years of age when I went for an interview. The Matron was unsmiling and certainly gave me no encouragement to start training. She put forward the long hours, hard work, sacrifices to be made' . . .*[66]

Undaunted Margery started her training:

> *'I felt very strange in my uniform – dress 9 inches from the floor, stiff white collar, stiff cuffs, starched white apron and a small starched cap perched on the top of my head! Oh, I forgot the black woollen stockings and black shoes'.*[66]

Joyce Akester wrote of her experiences as a student nurse in 1928:

> *'Our chief contact with the patients was the bed pan round. At that time most of the patients were in bed. Even a straight forward appendectomy was nursed in bed for 10 days . . . . We attended to "backs" and other pressure points every four hours, and any sign of a bed sore was a sign of inadequate care, and so a disgrace'.*[67]

In 1976, Guy's had celebrated the 250th anniversary of the opening of the Hospital and Her Majesty the Queen had opened Guy's Tower. In 1977, for the first time this event was celebrated by the first pictorial record in the Journal.

*The scene in the Colonnade when H.M. The Queen
arrived to open the Guy's Tower*

H.M. The Queen making her way to the Tower

The Queen opening the Guy's Tower

In 1979 a bumper edition of the Journal was published with many pages of tributes to Emily MacManus who had died the previous year.

A group of nurses with Emily MacManus

Centenarian Ellen Roadnight

From time to time the Journal reported on League Centenarians:

In 1982 it was Hilda Sullivan and 1984 Kate New, who had trained in the early years of the 20th century and were living links to the first years of the League.

Previously in 1981, Ellen Maud Roadnight who had trained in 1903 when Sarah Swift was Matron, celebrated her 100th birthday by a personal visit to Guy's, when she toured the wards in Hunt's House, the only clinical areas familiar to her.

1985 saw the first of many photos of a set re-union in the Journal. 30 members of the June 1962 met in 1984 from as far afield as Canada, Scotland and Cornwall. By 1988 there were nine set re-union reports and this trend had continued in every Journal since.

June 1962 Set Re-Union

Each year the editors worked hard to persuade members and others to write interesting articles for the Journal. This resulted in the readers learning much about the ever increasing number of nursing and medical developments, including counselling, care of the dying, geriatric health visiting, health promotion and the early days of the Nurse Practitioner, written about in 1981, almost twenty years before this became a familiar term in the NHS. Later there was the Night, later Site, Nurse Practitioner, Consultant Nurses and Modern Matrons.

This was the age of nurses with academic degrees and PhDs predicted so long ago in 1907.

They were also informed, amongst other things, about Nuclear Medicine, the role of the Hospital Superintendent, Peritoneal dialysis, the Oncology Department, the history of London Bridge and the Gordon Museum.

The League Journal has kept members informed and updated for 44 years, and through many momentous events, including the introduction of Salmon (the re-organisation of nursing administration), the demise of the Hospital Governors with the advent of the District Management Team, the mergers with Lewisham and St Thomas' Hospitals, the closure of the Guy's School of Nursing, the opening of the Tower Block and Thomas Guy House, the Save Guy's Campaign, the League receiving the Honorary Liberty of Southwark and finally the closure of the League itself.

The members learnt of this decision from President Vron Taylor. As she wrote at the time the decision was to go out with a bang not a whimper. Quoting Macbeth, she announced that the decision had been made to end the League in 2010:

'If it were done when 'tis done, then t'were well it were done quickly'.[68]

The editor sat back waiting for a flood of protests from members for the next Journal but in the end there was little, they accepted the decision with a resigned stoicism and in the 2007 Journal they learnt that July 10th 2010 was to be the date for the final celebratory AGM.

The Commemorative Journals in 1997 and 2001 recorded two major League celebrations in 1996 and 2000, but as the last Journal was published in 2009 it could not feature the final and biggest celebration of all at the final AGM on July 10th 2010. Instead this is recorded on a commemorative DVD and in the final chapter of this book.

Journal Editors

1966	J. Bennett, M. Calvert, A.M. Johnson, B. Warne, B. Whyte
1967–68	M. Calvert & J. Bennett
1969	B. Faulkner, E. Hodgson, E. Quealey, B. Randles, H. Smith, F. Taylor
1970–75 and 1978–79	Margaret Helliwell
1976–77	Pam Jefferies
1980–93	Barbara Stevenson
1994–2001	Mavis Fabling
2002	Celia Manson
2003	Lisa Burnapp
2004–10	Andie Howard

CHAPTER ELEVEN

Commemoration and Celebration

B etween 1996 and 2010 the League organised 3 major events. In 1996 to mark the last set of nurses to qualify at Guy's, in the year 2000 to celebrate the Millennium which coincided with the 100th birthday of the League and in July 2010 to celebrate the life of the League prior to its closure in December 2010.

The leading light for each of these celebrations was Betsy Morley, Chairman in 1996, President elect in 2000 and because of the success of the first two events; elected organiser for the 2010 AGM.

This is her account of the celebrations in 1996 and 2000.

Celebration 1996

The formation of the Nightingale Institute meant that the last trained Guy's nurses would qualify in 1996 and the League decided to make this a significant and celebrated event.

In April 1995 the planning began and it was recognised that it had to be done with sensitivity as emotions were running high. There was pride for the years during which Guy's had produced large numbers of skilled nurses; there was sadness at the loss of a training school whose prestigious name was known world wide and there was anger at what some saw as the needless destruction of a wonderful and lovingly remembered institution. It had to be a special day.

The start of the day was an easy decision – there had to be a celebratory service in Southwark Cathedral. We anticipated a congregation of about 500. After many hours of planning and visits to the Vice Provost we felt all the details had been considered. After much debate The Order of Service, the hymns, the anthem and the readings were agreed by Council.

Guy's main entrance around 1885

Then lunch; what was the best venue? A 'mad' idea emerged – why not cover the entire Consultants Car Park, the original entrance to the old Guy's Hospital, with a marquee, with the statue of Thomas Guy presiding over proceedings in the centre?

The whole courtyard covered by a huge marquee?

Was it feasible? Was it practical? Could we afford it?

The idea grew and became a reality. It was feasible and more or less practical and we could afford it – just! The marquee would provide lunch for 400 people, followed by a Gala evening with a dinner party followed by dancing in the Colonnade.

As the day drew near and the final stage of preparations started, the weather, previously quite mild and sunny, began to deteriorate. Major issues such as heating the marquee and the Colonnade became a last minute priority.

The picture above shows the courtyard in around 1885 – a nice empty space but by 1996 it had been the Consultants car park for many years. Their right to park there marked by a gold parking permit. To clear the area a space had been allocated in a nearby NCP car park and all gold permit holders informed but it would be a miracle if it happened.

Thursday 9th May arrived and not a car could be seen – it was one of our greatest achievements! The marquee was safely erected despite a force 10 gale and after some more last minute crises our day of celebration dawned.

The day, started with a service of celebration in Southwark Cathedral attended by, not 500, but 1200 Guy's nurses, their families and friends; requiring a quick scout round for extra chairs and the sharing of orders of service.

The address was given by the Very Reverend Colin Slee, Provost of Southwark, the anthem, sung by the augmented League choir, was 'Zadok the Priest' and there were readings by a newly qualified Guy's nurse and a League 'legend' Audrey Crump who read from Emily MacManus's book; 'Matron of Guy's'.

The guest of honour for the day was Emily MacManus' great niece also called Emily. We then returned to Guy's and a superb lunch in the marquee presided over by Thomas Guy himself.

Following lunch an exhibition had been prepared in the Robens Suite of Guy's memorabilia, photos, books, records, historical instruments and old uniforms just some of the items on display.

It was back to the marquee for the evening gala, champagne reception, dinner and finally dancing in the Colonnade. What a day!

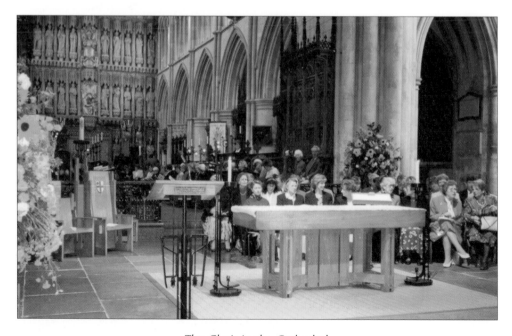

The Choir in the Cathedral

*Thomas Guy bedecked
with Guy's colours*

Lunch in the Marquee

The Exhibition

The Gala

Dancing in the Colonnade

The Figurine

At the 1995 AGM the League decided to celebrate the end of the Guy's School of Nursing but also to commemorate it in a permanent way. It was suggested that a porcelain figurine of a Guy's Staff Nurse dressed in uniform would be an appropriate and popular keepsake. Two Council members, President Margaret Lamb and Prue Bamlett (now Bosdet) agreed to take this project forward.

The Figurine

They approached the Royal Worcester Company as they had created a series of beautiful Sisters from London Hospitals in the 1960s.

Funding the project was a challenge as a £5,000 deposit was required when the contract was signed. In the event this was easily achieved as the response from League members was so enthusiastic and advance orders in their hundreds rolled in. Within sixteen months of the initial announcement a limited edition of 750 had been made and sold.

The sixteen months of design and production were a challenge for the two Council members. They were determined to ensure every detail was correct – including eight flukes in the nurse's cap, black lace up shoes that did not resemble Doc Martins and the correct colour for uniform and cape.

Getting the details just right meant delay and disappointment that the final figurine was not ready for the day of Celebration in May but by the autumn of 1996 all the figurines had been despatched to their proud new owners.

Celebration 2000

In the year 2000 the Country celebrated the Millennium and the League celebrated its centenary. To mark this anniversary a special day was planned to coincide with the Annual General Meeting on the 20th May.

Scarcely was the 1996 celebration over when planning began for the event in 2000.

Again the day started with a magnificent thanksgiving service in Southwark Cathedral and this was enjoyed by a large congregation, the address being given by the Bishop of Southwark and the augmented League choir singing 'I was glad' by Parry. At the end of the service seven kneelers made by League members were dedicated.

In the afternoon there was a large Victorian Fayre held in Atrium 1, a large open area in the recently opened Thomas Guy House, phase three of the Guy's post war rebuilding.

There were many stalls and displays and the stall holders had entered in to the spirit by dressing appropriately in Victorian costume. Cream teas were available with 1,000 scones home made by the League President and Chairman.

The Choir at the Cathedral Service

Victorian Fayre, Atrium 1

The evening's entertainment took the form of a revue based on 100 years of life at Guy's, featuring familiar faces from the past, well loved songs and repartee. It included some very sporting past house officers who sang songs from Residents Plays of the 1960s.

The theme of the evening was old time music hall and many of the audience dressed accordingly. Sketches portrayed good and not so good aspects of nursing in the 1950s and the present day and were greeted with much hilarity as well as providing some food for thought.

One of the highlights was the appearance of League Vice Chairman Vron Taylor, retired Director of Nursing and respected Justice of the Peace, dressed as Cupid, standing on one leg waving a bow and arrow and wearing a pink tunic and pink tights.

Verdict: A good day enjoyed by all.

The Review

The Bronze Sister

In 1997 a suggestion was made in Council to commission a bronze sculpture of a Guy's Sister to commemorate the League's centenary and as a lasting tribute to all Guy's nurses.

By 1998 it had been agreed that the bronze would be a half life size statue depicted wearing a Sister's uniform from the 1950s. Sculptor Sue Lamb accepted the commission and a Guy's Staff Nurse was chosen as a model. Work began in January 1999 and the sculpture was fashioned from the live model and photographs to ensure authenticity.

The cost of the sculpture was £5,500 and an appeal was launched to members to make a personal contribution towards the total. The names of all those who contributed were recorded in the 2001 Journal.

The Hospital Special Trustees offered a prime site to display the bronze in the Atrium on the second floor of Thomas' Guy House. The sculpture would be seen by dozens of people every day as it would be sited beside the main pedestrian access from London Bridge Station.

The Guy's Sister

*A cache pot was also commissioned
for the centenary*

The first public viewing was at the League's Centennial Celebration on May 20th 2000. The plan to bless the bronze on the day was not feasible but took place later in the summer on July 6th when Canon Andrew Nunn came and held a short service in the Atrium, attended by many Council members.

Miniature copies of the bronze were also made to order by the sculptor.

The Centennial Journal Competition

Members were invited to enter a competition to enhance the Commemorative Journal. Entries could be literary or artistic and a first prize of £250 was offered.

The first prize was a painting of the Guy's front gates by Patricia Glasswell

The second prize went to Monica Wakeham for a poignant tale of the last night of a young patient she had nursed entitled: 'Colin'.

The third prize went to Margo Lamb for a poem entitled 'Ode to a Cockroach' (in the past cockroaches were regularly seen during the night in the basements of old hospitals).

The Story of the Rose

Since the announcement of its closure in 2010, there had been much discussion about a lasting and memorable way to mark the end of the League. In 2005 Council member, Sally Hudson, a previous Honorary Secretary, suggested that a rose be named to commemorate the League and this was greeted enthusiastically by Council. It was agreed that the rose should be yellow/gold, the Guy's colours, and if possible with a good scent. After much research by Assistant Honorary Secretary, Gill Moore and visits by the Officers, a suitable rose was found at Harkness Roses, based in Hitchin, Hertfordshire. This was a hybrid T rose with a lovely gold colour and a delicate perfume. The working title for the rose was 'Guy's Gold'. The members were asked to approve this name for the rose or to suggest an alternative in the 2007 Journal and with no more suitable suggestions this was approved unanimously by Council.

Harkness launched the rose at the Chelsea Flower Show in 2008 but the League had a private preview on May 17th when Harkness sent a beautiful basket of Guy's Gold for the AGM.

The public introduction came at Chelsea on May 19th when Guy's gold was at the centre of the Harkness display.

Since then hundreds of Guy's Gold roses have been sold and appear in many League member's gardens. In 2010 Jill Johnstone and her husband donated 50 bushes in Kennington Park, South London. Four of these are to be part of a re-planting in the park as a memorial to 100 people who were killed locally in an air raid shelter that was bombed in October 1940.

Guy's Gold in Kennington Park

The Launch at Chelsea

The Final Celebration: July 10th 2010

Saturday July 10th dawned a delightfully hot and sunny day, the hoped for backdrop to the big day of Celebration for the League.

The organisers and helpers were up early to finalise preparations and receive last minute instructions. The stewards were briefed in the Burfoot Court Room and having received their identifying rosettes in the Guy's colours, they hurried off to the Cathedral to receive yet more instructions, before taking their places to direct and advise the expected crowds of League members, Guy's nurses and their families.

The choir arrived at the Cathedral at 10 am for their first and only rehearsal of the anthems and hymns. At Guy's there were early buyers at the sale in Atrium 2 hoping to have first pick at the many souvenirs on offer.

The Information Centre was set up in the Colonnade and some members arrived at Guy's early for coffee and to start a day of reminiscence by taking the historical tour of the Guy's site.

However the main event to start the day was building up in the Cathedral as tens, then hundreds and finally an estimated 1,500 people arrived for the service and packed in to the pews. Many said the service was the highlight of their day and it was a momentous occasion.

As part of his address, the Very Reverend Colin Slee, Dean of Southwark, commended the League for its brave decision to close and spoke about Guy's Gold, the rose commissioned in memory of the League:

> *'During this service we shall see a bowl of the Harkness rose, "Guy's Gold" brought to the altar. I think that is a fantastic way to mark the League's enduring impact. The "Peace" rose was named at the end of the Second World War; just imagine "Guy's Gold" flourishing and blooming in sixty-five years' time.*
>
> *Flowers at the foot of the altar make me want to say something important to the League. Thank you for setting an example to the Church of England. The Church is very bad at funerals; you set a splendid example this morning. The Church constantly starts things up and then fails to stop and bury them when they have completed their life. You have that courage. The nurses of the present school and hospitals are both of the past tradition and also of the future tradition. The League is doing something really important this morning, what one might call a mature decision! How I long for a Church of England with the maturity and decision you display, able to change and move as time requires change and movement to address present needs'.*

He continues his theme comparing the rose to League members.

> *'I looked up "Guy's Gold", named in honour of the Nurses' League. The catalogue says:*
>
> *'**ease of cultivation = robust'** – well nothing less would do, would it?*
>
> *'**Scent = mild'** – matron would disapprove if it were strong.*
>
> *'**This rose always looks fresh and cheerful'** – that's just what sister tutor taught us, isn't it?*
>
> *'**Colour tone is rich, eventually softening to light yellow'** – that's, almost, what we see gathered here this morning.*
>
> *'**The hybrid tea roses are making a strong comeback, from the heyday they enjoyed in the 1960s to 1980's** – I told you it was good to have met today's boat club* – (he had previously referred to rowing being revived at King's College).

'Always big and bold in the garden' – *anyone trained in this neighbourhood wouldn't be shy and retiring would they?*

'Perfect as cut flowers in the home' – *well, I think the modern, emancipated nurse, might tell her man, that no longer applies.*

'Be traditional and plant them in a bed together' – *I always found the traditional nurses' home was barred; it's the contemporary ones that plant them in a bed together; or be modern and mix them in borders.*

'. . . colour tone is rich . . . growth erect and densely branched' – *there can be no better expression of the wonderful kaleidoscopic, ethnic, gender, age and upbringing profile that King's, Guy's and St Thomas' nursing now exhibits to the world'.*[69]

Later in the service a tribute to the League from Betty Herbert, an iconic figure for League members was read to the congregation by Mavis Fabling:

'From the earliest pioneering days to the present time, Guy's nurses have served the community and the hospital. They have also been proud members of the Guy's Hospital Nurses' League, an organization providing them with friendship and support.

Since nurse training ceased at Guy's in 1996 and transferred to King's, London University, membership has inevitably decreased. Rather than experience a slow and painful decline, the conscious decision was taken to close the League.

Together with all of you, I feel very sad to witness the end of such a wonderful organization that was introduced 110 years ago by Dame Sarah Swift and has served Guy's nurses so well over such a long period.

As a tangible and beautiful reminder of all the Nurses' League has meant to us, "Harkness Roses" was commissioned to produce a very special rose, the Guy's Gold, to provide a legacy to a truly wonderful and greatly loved establishment.

I am so disappointed not to be with you to share in this day of celebration and commemoration. However, I shall be thinking of you and I send my best wishes to you all.

The following quotation by the late Dag Hammarskjold, Secretary General to the United Nations from 1953 to 1961 seems appropriate at this time:

'For all that has been . . . thanks

To all that shall be . . . yes'.

The flowers in the Cathedral, in Guy's colours, were beautiful

The basket of Guy's Gold blessed by the Dean

After the voices of the augmented League choir soared to the high notes of Handel's 'Zadok the Priest and the Guy's Gold rose had been blessed by the Dean, the service ended and it was off to lunch!

Atrium 1 at Guy's ready for diners

In the Robens Suite

Lunch was a prolonged affair as eating competed with chatting and catching up. After lunch many members attended the final AGM in a lecture theatre that seated 350 but saw at least 400, with all the stairs and aisles filled with people.

The AGM was conducted by the Acting President, Vron Taylor and included a reading of the names of members who had died in the previous year, the presentation of accounts, reports from the Benevolent & Scholarship Funds and news of the handover of funds to the Guy's & St Thomas' Charity.

Meanwhile, others sat in the Park walked round the Guy's site or visited the world renowned Gordon Museum. The lucky ones, who had secured early tickets, enjoyed a cream tea in the Colonnade.

After the AGM, the tight schedule of the day meant that members had the choice of listening to Dr Mike O'Brien's historical talk of Guy's or attending the auction of memorabilia. Both events were very well attended and much enjoyed.

The auction was in aid of Mercy Ships, and after much competitive bidding, raised over £3,500, which together with the sale of various smaller items and the collection from the Cathedral service, meant that the charity received £10,000. Mabel Chittock's medals raised £500 and Elsie Gladstone's £200.

Mabel Chittock's medals

Also at the auction were three Guy's figurines generously donated by members which sold for over £700 and a lovely scrap book from the early 1900s which went for £90. Items brought for auction on the day included a bottle of beer given to the nurses on the coronation in 1952 which went

The Auction

for £30. A painting by Patricia Glasswell that was raffled on the day made £500.

The day ended with a cocktail party in the Robens Suite with Guy's cocktails in blue and yellow (the Guy's colours) and two fantastic ice sculptures of the League Badge.

A memorable day, worthy of the final League AGM

Cream teas in the Colonnade

The Information Centre

Enjoying the Park

Patricia Glasswell's painting

The Cocktail Party

The magnificent ice sculpture at the cocktail party

GUY'S HOSPITAL NURSES' LEAGUE
CLOSES 31ST DECEMBER 2010

"I determined never to stop until I had come to the end
and achieved my purpose."

David Livingstone

References

1   Margaret Elizabeth Burt. BJN. 1931; Feb; 79(1951):31.
2   S.G, Nursing echoes, Nursing Record. 1893; Feb; 258, 67.
3   F. A. Sheldon, Guy's Hospital Trained Nurses' Institution, Maternity Charity and Midwifery Training School, Guy's Hospital Gazette. 1925; Bi-centenary Number; 139.
4   Charitable Sweating, BJN. 1892; Nov; 9(240): 890.
5   Editorial. BJN. 1892; Nov; 9 (240): 927.
6   Victoria Elizabeth Jones, 1935; Oct; 83(2007): 257.
7   Recreation Society minutes, LMA, 1901; Dec: H09/GY/R/01/002.
8   Sub-committee's report on proposed association.
9   Matron's report books, LMA, 1902, Feb: H09/GY/C/04/002.
10 Professional Review, BJN, 1902, Feb; 29 (746): 58.
11 Guy's Hospital Nurses' League, BJN, 1902; July; 29 (746): 60.
12 Editorial, BJN, 1905; Feb; 34 (877): 81.
13 Letters to the Editor, BJN, 1905; Feb: 34 (881): 138.
14 A Nursing Guide, 1904; 2nd edn.; pp. 79–80: Guy's Hospital Nurses' League.
15 Guy's Hospital Nurses' League Journal; 1985; Vol XX; 36.
16 The Hospital World, BJN, 1902; July; 29(744): 1–9.
17 Emily MacManus, Matron of Guy's, 1956; p. 39; Andrew Melrose Ltd.
18 Editorial, The Nursing Record, 1896; Nov; 17(449): 369.
19 The Guy's Hospital Nurses' League, BJN, 1913; April; 50(1308): 330–1.
20 League News, BJN, 1909; May; 42(1101): 369.
21 Guy's Hospital Nurses' League, BJN, 1910; May; 42(1153): 371.
22 Guy's Hospital Nurses' League, BJN, 1914; May; 52(1361): 387.
23 Guy's Hospital Nurses' League, BJN, 1918; May; 60(1573): 367.

24 Guy's Hospital Nurses' League, BJN, 1922; May; 68(1780): 298.

25 Guy's Hospital Nurses' League, BJN, 1911; May; 46(1205): 353.

26 Guy's Hospital Past & Present Nurses' League, BJN, 1923; May; 70 (1838): 316.

27 Guy's Hospital Nurses' League, BJN, 1925; June; 73(1888): 126.

28 Guy's Hospital Nurses' League Journal; 1987; Vol XX11; 15.

29 Guy's Hospital Nurses' League Journal; 1996; Vol XXX1; 31–2.

30 Emily MacManus, Matron of Guy's, 1956; pp. 107 & 114; Andrew Melrose Ltd.

31 Nursing Echoes, BJN, 1915; Sept; 55(1434): 256.

32 The College of Nursing: BJN, 1918; Sept; 61(1590): 183.

33 AGM and Honorary Secretary's Report , GHNL 1937–64, Supplement to the Nursing Guide; 1944: p. 13.

34 Guy's Hospital Nurses' League Journal; 2008; Vol XL111; 41–2.

35 Guy's Hospital Nurses' League Journal; 2006; Vol XL1; 42.

36 260th Council minutes, Guy's Hospital Nurses' League, Hospital News; Jan; 1985: 2.

37 Guy's Hospital Nurses' League Journal; 1987; Vol XX11; 10.

38 288th Council minutes, Letter included with minutes; Guy's Hospital Nurses' League, July; 1994.

39 A Nursing Guide, 1904, 2nd ed. Nursing News; p. 98.

40 Emily MacManus, Obituary for Mabel Bonsor; GHNL 1937–64, Supplement to the Nursing Guide; 1944.

41 Emily MacManus, Obituary for Louise Haughton; GHNL 1937–64, Supplement to the Nursing Guide; 1954: 9.

42 Guy's Hospital Nurses' League Journal; 1972; Vol VII; 35.

43 Guy's Hospital Nurses' League Journal; 1996; Vol XXX1; 24 & 29.

44 Fabling, M., Salmon, M. K. Nursing at Guy's. Cambridge: Granta Editions; 1997.

45 A Nursing Guide, 1902, 1st ed. Preface.

46 Nursing Guide, 1904, 2nd ed. Nursing as a Profession, pp. 5–6.

47 A Nursing Guide, 1937, 12th ed. The Nursing Profession, pp. 5–6.

48 A Nursing Guide, 1950, 13th ed. Register of Nurses, p. 165.

49 Sister Kiddle, Interesting letters from the front; GHNL 1914–1935, Supplement to the Nursing Guide; 1914: p. 26.

50 Christmas in the Hospital, GHNL 1914–35, Supplement to the Nursing Guide; 1929: p. 28.

51 Garden Party at the Cottage, GHNL 1914–35, Supplement to the Nursing Guide; 1930: p. 23.

52 GHNL 1937–64, Supplement to the Nursing Guide; 1941: p. 4.

53 Emily MacManus; Matron's Christmas letter, GHNL 1941; Dec.

54 Emily MacManus; Matron's Christmas letter; GHNL 1937–64, 1942.

55 Dorothy M. Smith; Impressions of the Coronation; GHNL 1937–64, Supplement to the Nursing Guide, 1953: pp. 7–9.

56 Phyllis Buckley; Down into the Zambezi Valley, News sheet, GHNL 1937–64; Supplement to the Nursing Guide; 1955: p. 18.

57 Newsheet, GHNL 1937–64, Supplement to the Nursing Guide; 1961.

58 Lord Robens, Guy's Hospital Nurses' League Journal; 1; 1966.

59 Diary of an in patient, Guy's Hospital Nurses' League Journal; 1; 1966.

60 Elizabeth Searle, Guys to Ghana-and back, Guy's Hospital Nurses' League Journal; V111; 1973: 41.

61 Wendy Myers, Sister in the Solomons, Guy's Hospital Nurses' League Journal; X; 1975: 37 & 39.

62 Wendy Myers, Health in the Himalayas, Guy's Hospital Nurses League Journal; X1V; 1979: 45.

63 Marny Hallam, Thirty Years On, Guy's Hospital League Journal; X; 1975: 43.

63a Marny Hallam, Thirty Years On, Guy's Hospital Nurses' League; XI; 1976: 18.

64 Barbara Watson, One Is . . ., Guy's Hospital Nurses' League Journal; XV; 1980: 26.

65 Dorothy I. Norman, Looking Back to 1934; Guy's Hospital Nurses' League Journal; X111; 1978: 25.

66 Margery Poyser, My Nursing Career 1921–48; Guy's Hospital Nurses' League Journal; XV; 1980: 37.

67 Joyce Akester, Sixty Years Ago; Guy's Hospital Nurses' League Journal; XXV; 1990: 39.

68 Vron Taylor; The Future of the League, Guy's Hospital Nurses' League Journal; XL; 2005: 12.

69 Very Reverend Colin Slee, Dean of Southwark, Sermon at Guy's Hospital Nurses' League Celebration, Southwark Cathedral website; July 10th 2010.

Officers of the League 1900–2010

President
1900–44	Lady Mabel Bonsor
1944–57	Lady Cunliffe
1957–78	Emily MacManus
1979–82	Dorothy Smith
1983–89	Doreen Sinclair-Brown
1989–95	Betty Herbert
1996–2000	Margaret Lamb
2001–03	Betsy Morley
2004–06	Vron Taylor
2007–10	Pam Jefferies

Honorary Secretary
1900–09	Dame Sarah Swift
1910–17	Louisa Haughton
1917–27	Margaret Hogg
1928–46	Emily MacManus
1946–53	Dorothy Smith
1953–62	Jean Recknell
1963–69	Ann Johnson
1969–71	Linda Titley
1972–83	Betty Herbert
1984–95	Barbara Stevenson
1995–96	Mavis Fabling
1996–2001	Sally Hudson
2001–10	Laura Byers

Assistant Honorary Secretary
1937–43	Frances Sheldon
1944–62	Evelyn Cawthorne
1963–76	Joan Blackwell
1976–79	Barbara Stevenson / Jean Baker
1980–94	Muriel Thiesen
1996–96	Sally Hudson
1998–2000	Jill Johnstone
2000–10	Gill Moore

Chairman
1900–10	Sir Henry Cosmo Bonsor
1910–25	Viscount Goschen
1925–39	Lady Mabel Bonsor
1939–45	Lady Cunliffe
1947–57	Kitty Bulleid
1957–69	Florence Taylor
1969–73	Linda Titley
1974–79	Doreen Sinclair-Brown
1979–83	Barbara Stevenson
1984–88	Betty Herbert
1989–92	Joan Page
1993–97	Betsy Morley
1998–2003	Lisa Burnapp
2004–10	Alison Russell

Treasurer
1900–03	Mrs Shaw
1904–06	Mrs Bryant
1907–15	Mrs Fagge
1915–20	Mrs Cameron
1920–30	Mrs Hughes
1930–36	Mrs Ogilvie
1930–39	Mrs Davies-Colley
1939–63	Kathleen Shackle
1963–73	Viven Blaikley
1974–79	Pip Salmon
1979–95	Faith Rigby
1996–2001	Marian Hubble
2001–10	Doreen Stebbing

Assistant Honorary Treasurer
2000–01	Jill Johnstone
2002–10	Julia Freeman

APPENDIX 2

Guy's Hospital Nurses' League Constitution

1. Title:
The League shall be called the Guy's Hospital Nurses' League.

2. Aims:
The aims of the League shall be:
   i. To promote social and professional interests between past and present nurses.
  ii. To publish a Register of Members and an annual Journal.
 iii. To provide support and assistance to members in need.
 iv. To provide financial assistance for nurses wishing to further their professional education through the Sir Cosmo and Lady Mabel Bonsor Scholarship Fund and the Dorothy Holland Educational Grant.

3. Membership:
There shall be three categories:
   i. Full membership, available to:
     a. All Guy's trained nurses, including those who trained at the Guy's and Lewisham Training School.
     b. Nurses who trained elsewhere who have completed one year within the Guy's and St. Thomas' Hospital Trust.
  ii. Free membership is conferred upon all members on reaching their sixty-fifth birthday.
 iii. Honorary membership, accorded to such persons connected with or having been connected with Guy's, as may be invited by the Council.

4. Subscriptions:
   i. The annual subscription for membership shall be decided by the Council and published in the League Journal.
  ii. Members whose subscription is in arrears and who have been duly notified thereof shall cease to be members but are welcome to rejoin at any time.

5. Privileges of Membership:
Subject to Council approval, every member:
   i. Is eligible for the support and assistance set out in paragraph 2: 'Aims of the League'.

ii.   Will receive a copy of the League Journal, and Register.

iii. Will be notified of social functions arranged by the Council.

6. Annual General Meeting:

This shall usually take place in May and the details and agenda will be published in the Journal.

The meeting will be asked to approve an audited statement of the accounts.

7. Sub-committees and Special Representatives of the League:

   i.   Sub-committees of the League will be set up to reflect the activities of the League as set out in paragraph 2: 'Aims of the League'. Some sub-committees will be permanent, but the number and constitution of sub-committees will vary according to the duties that each is required at any particular time in the life of the League.

  ii.   Each sub-committee will be led by a Special Representative, who will also be the Secretary of the sub-committee, and he/she will be approved by Council. At least one Honorary Officer must be included in each sub-committee. A sub-committee may not be required to support every activity of the League and the appointment of a Special Representative with sole responsibility may, therefore, be approved instead.

 iii.   Special Representatives will be responsible for:

   a.   Attending Council meetings and maintaining channels of communication by requesting tabled agenda time for reporting back.

   b.   Forming the sub-committee (if required) and organising meetings as appropriate.

   c.   Ensuring that the purpose of the sub-committee is fully expedited.

8. Officers of the League:

   i.   These shall be:

The President	The Honorary Treasurer
The Chairman	The Honorary Assistant
The Vice Chairman	Treasurer
	The Honorary Secretary
	The Honorary Assistant Secretary

  ii.   Method of Election and Terms of Service:

   a.   The President shall be elected for a period of three years. ##Names proposed by Council will be published in the Journal of the year prior to the commencement of The President's term of office. A postal vote will then take place from the General Membership to be completed by the end of April of the same year. The name of the successful candidate will be announced at the AGM in May of that year. The elected candidate will serve as President Elect for three years prior to taking up the office of President.

   b.   The Council is empowered to nominate Honorary Members. Voting will take place annually at the October meeting.

c. At its first meeting after the Annual General Meeting, the Council shall appoint from among its members the following officers, being full members of the League, unless otherwise stated, for voting at the October meeting, with terms of office as stated:

A Vice Chairman

An Honorary Treasurer   An Honorary Assistant Treasurer
An Honorary Secretary   An Honorary Assistant Secretary

All the above to serve for five years and eligible for re-election for a period of one further term of office.

9. The Council:

i. The affairs of the League shall be under the control of a Council consisting of the following:

The Chairman   The President
The Vice Chairman   The Vice Presidents
The Honorary Treasurer   Privileged Members
The Honorary Secretary
The Honorary Assistant Treasurer
The Honorary Assistant Secretary
The Special Representative for each sub-committee.
Three Honorary Members**
Twelve representatives of Past and/or Present Nursing Staff**
**Elected by Council to serve for three years.

ii. Any vacancy occasioned by the resignation or death of a member, including co-opted members, may be filled by a nominee of the Council to serve for the remainder of the term concerned.

iii. The names of the members of the Council shall be published annually in the League Journal.

iv. The Council shall meet once in every three months and at such other times as may be considered necessary by the Honorary Secretary or by two Members of the Council. Meetings shall be summoned with not less than seven days' notice, the notice to include the proposed Agenda. A quorum shall be considered to be one third of the Council.

v. At the meeting preceding the Annual General Meeting, the Council shall consider the audited statement of income and expenditure prepared by the Honorary Treasurer in readiness for submission of the approved accounts to the full membership of the Annual General Meeting.

vi. The League Constitution should be reviewed on a five-yearly basis or more frequently if required.

vii. While maintaining control of the funds and property of the League and responsibility for the form, content and issue of the Register and power to make or modify the rules of the League, the Council may look for advice on matters of detail, particularly such as relate to property and finance, to an Executive Committee.

viii. Privileged Membership of Council is a privilege bestowed upon an individual who has made an exceptional contribution to the work of the Council over and above the requirements of the role/office held.

ix. Method of election and terms of service:

    a. Nominations may be put forward by any League member to an Officer of the League and must be carried by a majority vote at the Officers' meeting in order to be taken forward to Council. The Chairman has the casting vote.

    b. Nominations must be discussed at an Officers' meeting, in the absence of the nominee, prior to the April Council meeting where formal election will take place. Membership will commence in July of the same year.

    c. Nominees must only be approached following the decision made at the Officers' meeting and prior to the April Council meeting.

    d. A brief citation about the nominee must be provided to support the nomination. Names of successful nominees will be announced at the May AGM following election in April.

    e. Privileged members of Council may attend Council meetings and hold voting rights.

10. The Executive Committee:

  i. This shall comprise:

    The President
    The Chairman
    The Vice Chairman
    The Honorary Treasurer
    The Honorary Secretary
    The Honorary Assistant Treasurer
    The Honorary Assistant Secretary

  ii. The Executive Committee shall meet as often as is necessary on notice from the Honorary Secretary and will report back to the next meeting of the Council. Three members shall constitute a quorum for meetings.

11. Amendment to the Rules:

These rules may be added to, repealed or amended by the Council of the League by resolution requiring the agreement of two thirds of those present and voting.

  \# There will be no President Elect from 2006. The President has been elected until the end of 2010.

\#\# The Chairman will now remain in office until the end of 2010.

At the April 2007 Council meeting it was unanimously agreed to allow Council members, at the end of their statutory three year term, to remain on Council until the end of 2010, without being nominated or taking a break of one year.

The Constitution was amended by Council on 25th April 2007.

Index